EMERGENCY!

EMERGENCY!

SAUNDRA SHOHEN
and ANN LORING

ST. MARTIN'S PRESS/NEW YORK

Except for the known public figures mentioned in this work, all of the characters are either entirely fictitious or composites of several different people, and all names except for those of known public figures are fictitious. Any resemblance between characters in this account, except for recognized public figures, and any actual persons living or dead is strictly coincidental and without the knowledge of the authors or the publisher.

EMERGENCY! Copyright © 1989 by Saundra Shohen and Ann Loring. All rights reserved. Printed in the United States of America. No part of this book may be used or reproduced in any manner whatsoever without written permission except in the case of brief quotations embodied in critical articles or reviews. For information, address St. Martin's Press, 175 Fifth Avenue, New York, N.Y. 10010.

Design by Jaye Zimet

Library of Congress Cataloging-in-Publication Data

Shohen, Saundra.
    Emergency! : behind the emergency doors of a New York City hospital / Saundra Shohen in collaboration with Ann Loring.
      p. cm.
    "A Thomas Dunne book."
    ISBN 0-312-03330-3
    1. Hospitals—New York (N.Y.)—Emergency services. 2. Emergency medical services—New York (N. Y.) 3. Roosevelt Hospital (New York, N.Y.) I. Loring, Ann. II. Title.
RA975.5.E5S48 1989
362.1'8'097471—dc20   89-34850

First Edition

10 9 8 7 6 5 4 3 2 1

Kudos to all of the doctors and nurses and paramedics and important others in the Emergency Department at St. Luke's Roosevelt Hospital Center who care—all of the time.

CONTENTS

CONTENTS

THE LANGUAGE

As in every profession, medical people have a language of their own. Although glossaries usually appear at the end of a book, this one is here so the reader will not have to be stopped in mid-drama while I explain what a word means in "doctor talk."

Bus: the ambulance

Charge nurse: person responsible for all nursing functions and nursing personnel on a specific shift

Code Room: trauma room with specialized lifesaving equipment

CPR: cardiopulmonary resuscitation

Emergent: describing life and death situations needing immediate attention

EMT: emergency medical technician

E.R.: Emergency Room (in the 1980s, beginning to be known as Emergency Department)

Gurney:	collapsible stretcher on wheels used in ambulance
Head nurse:	person in charge of all nursing functions and nursing personnel on the unit at all times
House:	the hospital
Intubation:	passage of a plastic tube through the mouth into the windpipe to assist breathing
I.V.:	intravenous line inserted in a patient's vein to replenish vital fluids
Nonurgent:	can wait, if necessary
Page unit:	beeper used to reach people STAT
Paramedic:	specially trained ambulance technician; performs more duties than the EMT
Shift:	hospital shifts are designated as 8 A.M. to 4 P.M., 4 P.M. to midnight, midnight to 8 A.M.
STAT:	immediately
Triage:	procedure of designating patients for speed of treatment depending upon their condition (emergent, urgent, nonurgent)
Urgent:	serious situations needing attention as soon as possible

1 THE HOSPITAL

James Henry Roosevelt, the founder of Roosevelt Hospital, was born into wealth and position in 1800. Intelligent, handsome, athletic, he seemed set for a life of smooth success as a lawyer, and of pleasure as a member of New York society. However, in 1830, Roosevelt suffered a severe illness—it is not clear whether this was a result of lead poisoning from medicine wrongly administered for a minor complaint, or poliomyelitis. In any event, it left him badly crippled.

His law career was at an end. He broke his engagement. He settled into an almost reclusive existence, dictated as much by his choice as by the difficulty he had in moving around. Eventually, however, he found a goal, and it was one that made him change his manner of living. He became totally austere and frugal. Roosevelt was pursuing a dream: He wanted to build up enough of a financial pyramid so that upon his death there would be sufficient funds to endow a hospital for the care of those sick people who were unable to pay for private medical services.

He succeeded. By careful saving and shrewd investment, Roosevelt's estate grew, until at the time of his death, it was estimated to be almost a million dollars—in those days, enough to initiate the process of building a hospital.

1

Eight years later, in 1869, the funds had multiplied and ground was broken for what is now one of the buildings of this large urban hospital complex. The building was dedicated in November of 1871.

The New York *Herald* carried the story the next day, headlined A MONSTER MONUMENT OF CHARITY. "This noble symbol," it read, "of Mr. Roosevelt's industry and beneficence, when entirely completed, will be the finest institution of its kind on this continent, if not in the world."

Roosevelt Hospital has grown since that day in 1871. (In 1979 it merged with St. Luke's Hospital.) It now cares for 370,000 patients a year, the number of people living in the state of Vermont!

As it true of all large inner-city hospitals now, the resources of St. Luke's Roosevelt's Emergency Department are strained to bursting because the department must function as more than a center for trauma treatment. It is where visitors to the city and the poor of the city go for medical care. This voluntary, not-for-profit hospital emergency department is sometimes used in place of a private doctor. So, true to James Roosevelt's dream, Roosevelt Hospital's Emergency Department is busy twenty-four hours a day, every day of the year, handling with speed, efficiency, and dedication the accident cases, the patients with sudden severe illness, the victims of violent crime—and the treatment of "those sick people who are unable to pay for private medical service."

A granite monument stands on the grounds of the hospital. It bears the name of the Roosevelt family and the motto *Qui Plantavit Curabit:* He who has planted will care for.

2 THE STAFF

THE DOCTORS

Emergency medicine has become a specialty, like oncology, cardiology, or pediatrics. The men and women who choose this field are like fighter pilots: Emergency medicine involves constant unexpected events, and the doctors have to be capable of making immediate and difficult decisions.

Deciding on a specialty can be confusing for many medical students. Some of them spend nights, weeks, months, even years agonizing over it. But the doctors who become E.D. specialists seem very clear in their choice. In the rotation through the various hospital departments, which is part of their training, they get a taste of the life there—in many ways unique—and they like it. Where most medical students hate their rotation through the E.D. because everything moves at such a fast pace, decisions have to be made in a hurry, and the pressure is just about constant, the potential E.D. specialist loves it.

George Phillips is typical of the kind of doctors we get in emergency medicine. In his late thirties, he had been preparing for this, in a way, since he was seven years old.

3

Now, in his slacks and white lab coat over a white shirt, hospital I.D. clipped to his shirt, stethoscope stuffed into his pocket along with his rubber hammer and pencil flashlight, he is the very model of an emergency medicine specialist. Also, he is in an urban hospital emergency department that treats sixty-five thousand patients every year. He is fast and good and caring and compassionate. The patients and their families love him. The doctors and nurses respect him. He has been working for many years, knowing for most of that time that he would become a surgeon and then an emergency medicine physician. And a good one. He fits right into the 7-day-a-week, 24-hour-a-day, 365-days-a-year world of the E.R.

Then there is Tina Lawrence, a tiny and very business-like young woman who makes her presence felt through her psychological and physical strength. She is a no-nonsense, diagnose, treat-and-admit, or treat-and-release kind of doctor.

It was hard for Tina to understand why some male patients had an embarrassing moment when she entered the room and started an examination. Business was business, and she was a damned good doctor. Her judgments were right on target. She cared on a deep level for the pain and suffering she saw. That's why she was there. She wanted to help. Taking time for a long chat was out, however. She always made sure that the patient understood the ramifications of the medical problem for which he or she was being treated. She always went over, in detail, any issues to do with medications, but she left the superfluous reassurances to the nurses.

Perhaps having four brothers who were cops and who always felt they had to take care of her had something to do with it. Her sense of independence and her need for it were well served by her becoming a physician. While some women felt they were "breaking new ground" by taking up medicine in a world of men, Tina had her own reasons.

Long hours, tough decisions, patients with splinters and patients with knives jutting out between their shoulder blades—one either chooses to be in the E.R. and loves the challenge of it, or one tolerates it and waits for the day to come when it's time to move on to the next department. Tina is here to stay.

For those doctors who love it and choose it, the E.R. feels just right. They take the pungent odors and the long hours in their stride. They make sound decisions. They feel good about what they do for their patients in that setting, and the families of the patients seem to feel good about it, too. These doctors know what they're doing and the patients know they know. No matter how complex the case, it's handled. Their satisfaction comes from being involved in many of the most important and dramatic medical cases the hospital sees.

THE NURSES

Bag ladies and alcoholics, stabbings and shootings, thousands of incontinent patients, thousands of vomitous patients, untold heart-attack victims, car-accident victims, self-inflicted wounds, and wailing family members—one would think that years of this would send the strongest, most professional nurse running for the hills.

Here in the E.D., however, one finds a cadre of dedicated nurses who never give up hope, always feeling there is a solution to whatever condition they see; who teach each other what to do when their patience for their patients runs out—how to come back the next day and feel renewed, how never to stop caring about the people who need them.

When they are low, when they feel that for their families

and for their patients they have become an endless teat that must never run dry, this role of nourisher seems ultimately to give them great satisfaction. It's true that every now and then, the nurses will feel that they aren't able to "take it all in, chew it up, digest it, and go on to the next" as well as they used to. Maybe the burnout that everyone talks about is really happening. Maybe they feel frustrated. Maybe they occasionally think about a new experience in another place, perhaps even in another country.

Usually, those thoughts occur on a bad day. And when the next day dawns, the E.R. nurses are where they are drawn to be, where they are a mainstay, where they are so needed, every day, every shift, 365 days, evenings, and nights a year.

THE HOUSEKEEPERS

We don't always notice them, but they're there, all the time, and doing a rather thankless job. Sweeping up the candy wrappers and other debris thoughtless people leave on the waiting-room floor is the least of it. Cleaning up the public rest rooms, which occasionally hold surprises, mopping up the vomit and the blood and God knows what else is part of the job in the E.D. In fact, it is *their* job in the E.D. And these folks must constantly work around sounds and sights that were never a part of their training. They are not immune to the pain and suffering and death and the effort to save life. They are, in fact, quite tuned in to it. But has anyone ever asked someone on the Emergency Department housekeeping staff, "And how was your day today—was it a difficult day for you?"

THE SECURITY GUARDS

The guards assigned to the E.R. know that it can be the craziest, weirdest, strangest setting in the hospital. It is certainly the area with the most action. These guards are strong and quiet and insightful. They are keenly aware of everyone who comes and goes. They notice everyone in the waiting room, and they generally know for whom these people are waiting. They've got to be alert when the media show up during a breaking news story. They've got to be compassionate when a waiting relative is pacing desperately in anticipation of hearing bad news. They've got to keep an air of authority for those occasional troublemakers who would disturb the peace. They've got to be fast, fair, and sensible—and they are.

THE SOCIAL WORKERS

Social workers are a vital part of a hospital's staff. Commonly, many are assigned to the patient floors, where they perform such services as helping people plan for home care after they are discharged. Others train their newer colleagues for dealing with the dynamics of illness and its effects on the patient's family. Usually, however, the last place a social worker expects to be working is in the Emergency Department. Many social workers do best when they deal with people who come in for appointments at a prearranged time. Although hospitals don't provide that amenity very often in any area, those workers dealing with in-patients and their families are in familiar-enough territory not to feel displaced.

Not in the E.D.! The social workers who choose the Emergency Department definitely self-select it. They thrive in an atmosphere where everything happens quickly, unexpectedly, and often dramatically. They are emotionally rewarded when they handle crisis intervention for a rape victim, advice for a young father left with a nursing baby, for an elderly woman who has been mugged, or for a person with AIDS. That's their fulfillment, their satisfaction with their interaction with people in a time of need. It's not unusual to hear a social worker say that that's what social work was meant to be.

One of these dedicated professionals is considering writing a paper on the impact of the social worker in the Emergency Department. It will be subtitled *Reflections of a Believer.*

3 BEGINNINGS

It could be a party in a SoHo loft—wall-to-wall people talking, drinking, laughing, reminiscing, and, threading through it all, the loud incessant drumbeat of rock music.

It is not.

On this Thursday evening in March of 1981, I am dancing and celebrating in the hallway of the Roosevelt Hospital Emergency Room, which closed its doors just a few hours ago. Hard to believe it's the same hallway that I was used to seeing congested with patients lying on stretchers; anxious families clustering around; some patients protesting for attention, others sitting nervously awaiting their turn; doors being pushed open and medics clattering in and out. The rooms have lost their identity. All of the modern medical equipment is gone, moved to a temporary Emergency Department setting on the grounds of the hospital. Construction will begin tomorrow for a new state-of-the-art facility. The Code Room, each day the battleground of life and death forces, has been transformed into a bar. The examining rooms are set up with row upon row of tables, laden with all kinds of home-cooked foods: gnocchi, weirdly shaped pastas, pirogen, reflecting the multi-ethnic origins of the people who work in the E.D.

Everywhere I see faces I know, faces of people I have

shared time with during these past few years—all of the E.D. staff. The nurses, suddenly sexually attractive in their cocktail dresses, the ambulance drivers, the police who so often come in with accident cases and psychos, now looking oddly unrecognizable in slacks and sweaters in place of their uniforms, the only clue to their occupation is the bulge their guns make under their overhanging shirts. The firemen are there, as well as politicians and celebrities. There are also all the specialties of physicians, interns, administrators, secretaries, and aides from the many departments throughout the hospital.

I drift off toward what used to be the waiting room for our patients. I peer in. The room is empty. The paint is peeling and there are mute, somewhat cleaner geometric spaces set sharply against the grime of the walls where posters and notices once hung. The inevitable dust-encrusted rubber plant is gone. The old tatty chairs have been removed. The door is locked.

Standing there, I notice that the party noises dim out and I become aware of a soft silent echo, the ghostlike residue of the countless patients who have passed through this setting, "cases," from the birth and abandonment of a newborn John Doe to the emblazoning death of John Lennon. Particles of their remembered agony and fear film the walls of this room with a fine layer of history. How many of us look back at our adolescence and say, "Whoever would have thought then that I'd be doing what I'm doing now?" I think almost everyone—all but those lucky few who have known since childhood just exactly what they wanted to do in their lives and have been able to go ahead and do it.

When I had my first job, working in a laundry after school, the thought that I would be where I am now would have been fantastic. A childhood that was peripatetic when my parents were together (my father was an FBI agent whose assignments took him all over the country, and my mother and I trailed after), and close to real poverty when they parted, hardly prepared me for anything.

But my love of school and studying held me in good stead when, as the mother of two children, I found work writing, then editing, and earned my master's degree while I was working.

I spent many years working in the administrative end of a child guidance center and then moved on. Next stop was Roosevelt Hospital, administrative manager of their social work department. When I was offered the job of administrator of the Emergency Department, I didn't hesitate. My early years had given me a great deal of insight and sensitivity to other people's frailties and problems, and I was confident that my most valuable experiences in life, both personally and professionally, grew out of the moments when I helped others. I was ready.

AROUND THE CLOCK . . .

THE EMERGENCY DEPARTMENT

Doctors and nurses, social workers and respiratory therapists, and security guards. Emergency medical technicians, clerks, housekeepers, paramedics, volunteers. Rooms and monitors and stretchers and crash carts and casts and crutches and defibrilators and the locked narcotics cabinet. Ringing phones and air-paging and moans and sirens. And human beings in every kind of pain and agony; lives saved and lives lost, tears and—occasionally—laughter.

The nurse opened the blanket.

"Jesus!"

It was the first time, in the ten days since I had started as administrator, that I'd seen anything shake this nurse's professional composure. Bea Olsen had been working here for more than ten years. She was a large, comfortable woman and a superb nurse, able to handle whatever came up, no matter how bizarre. In my ten days, there had, of course, been numerous casualties, ranging from severe asthma to emergent heart attacks. All difficult, serious admissions. Bea was a paragon—cool, collected, efficient, and caring even in the most chaotic situations.

The ambulance driver was holding the blanket extended in his arms as though proffering a grotesque gift. There, in a large cellophane bag, already packed in ice, were two feet!

The once-white running sneakers in which they were shod were now an encrusted, blood-soaked brown, the yellow socks drenched, the raw ends of human ankles, of nerve and muscle and flesh, lay there, cleaved so sharply that not even the lisle threads of the socks had begun to unravel.

"Jesus, the feet are here, but where the hell is the patient?"

"He's in the second ambulance with the paramedics; they're bringing him in now."

"Is he stabilized enough to be transferred?" That was Dave Goldberger, the doctor.

"Yeah."

"I'll take a fast look and then we'll get him the hell to Bellevue!"

Bellevue Hospital was then one of the few hospitals in the city that had a microsurgery team: the best. If anyone could reattach the severed feet, they could.

Dave shook his head. "Poor guy. I don't think even they can do it." He peered into the blanket again. "Too damned much tissue damage. But let's give him every chance. We'll get him over there pronto, soon as the bus arrives."

The ambulance driver, cradling the blanket, raced for the exit just as the second paramed bus pulled into the courtyard.

I raced for the nearest bathroom.

Bea came in after me. "That was a tough one." She put a trembling arm on my shoulder.

"What's going to happen to him? Do you think Bellevue can help? I'd like to call there and . . ."

"Forget it! No call. They'll do what they have to. They'll do everything they can. And lady, no follow-up on cases after they leave our E.R." It was a preemptory order. "Understand? It'll kill you if you do. Conserve your energy."

I shuddered. "Oh God, I'm going to dream about this."

"No, you're not." She was once more the calm, collected, efficient nurse. "We're going out for a drink later. We'll talk about it, vomit it up in words." She walked me to the door. "That's our therapy. No bad dreams."

The waves of nausea were slowly receding. The sweat on my face slowly cooling. And I thought, What am I doing here in this job? How did I arrive here? I had started this work with confidence; now I didn't know whether I'd be able to face all of these raw manifestations the human condition deals out. I wasn't at all sure.

■ ■ ■

An actor is rushed into the E.R. with a deep gash in his scalp that extends almost down to his forehead. He is bleeding profusely. A blood-saturated Turkish towel is jammed tightly against the wound.

Well, I think, there is certainly more than one way to let an actor know that you don't like the performance they've given.

Seriously, though, the experience that brings this actor into the hospital is no joke—far from it. It was a frightening, almost fatal attack. What is even more frightening to learn is that this patient is not the first victim of this kind of attack. At least four other people have been felled in the exact spot by a man whom the police have eloquently and judiciously christened "the rock-tossing maniac." This man has been terrorizing the Times Square theater district for a year. The police explain that this "crazy" crouches on the rooftops of buildings, waits for an innocent passerby, and then hurtles a huge cinder block down.

Our actor, an understudy in a current play, had already

checked into the theater for the evening show and found, once again, that the player for whose role he was standing by was almost finished with his makeup and was preparing to go onstage.

The understudy thought he might catch a breath of air and console himself with a smoke. As was his responsibility, he notified the stage manager that he was stepping outside the door and that if anything unusual happened—if his fellow actor had a heart attack or broke his knee or threw a convulsive fit—he would be within three feet of the theater.

He was standing in the alleyway ready to light up when . . .

"I got this funny feeling that someone was watching me."

Suddenly this huge thing came smashing down, sideswiping his head and striking him across the shoulder. The next thing he remembered was looking up, to see a crowd of people surrounding him and hearing the voice of our EMT saying, "Take it easy now. Easy. You're going to be okay."

Fifteen stitches later, with the assurance that there will be but a hairline scar, our actor is ready to be released.

Well, maybe the publicity (the story, I know, will hit all of the papers and TV) will reward him with a juicy part of fifty-two sides in a long-running Broadway hit.

The actor turns, grasps our hands, thanks us each in turn for the care we've given him, and leaves with a happy exit line.

"I'm lucky to be alive!"

■   ■   ■

A cool brisk fall morning. I walk in long rapid strides to the hospital, aware that confronting me on my desk is a barrage of papers awaiting my attention.

I sigh, breathe the too-crisp air, and think, *Order. Today I shall restore order,* and I begin to sort out memos, notes, record sheets. I'll finish all my paperwork, all my filing, all my . . ."

No sooner do I seat myself than the phone rings loudly and impudently.

"Up and at 'em," a voice shouts out from the E.R. phone. "Get ready. We're receiving a bunch of injured kids here soon."

Later, the teacher chaperoning this elementary-school class tells me what happened.

It began with a fairly routine trip into the city. An elementary-school class, about twenty youngsters on the school bus accompanied by their teacher and a vice-principal, "Lewis and Clarking" their way into Manhattan for a day at the museum.

The bus driver, an old pro who knows of a back road or two, makes excellent time and the kids arrive about twenty minutes before the huge entrance doors are opened.

The kids scramble out of the bus onto the back parking lot and begin to cluster off into small groups, to explore.

The day is cooler than predicted, the chill in the air a bit nippier than the inside of the bus, and some of the youngsters are not dressed warmly enough.

One creative youngster spies steam coming out of a grating in the ground close to the side of the building. He rushes over to it, places his hands on his hips and establishes his right to this space.

"Come on—come over here. There's hot air. I'll let some of you share with me. Come on."

Six more shivering little elves skedaddle over to stand in the warm drafts of air. They begin to stomp their feet and dance over the metal grating. They are laughing and having a great time.

Suddenly, all seven disappear.

With a groaning, crunching sound, the grating gives way and the children have fallen—God knows how many feet—into the sewer system.

Fortunately, the teacher stays calm. She rounds up the

rest of her class and stands over the abyss consoling the children caught below. She keeps up a running patter of talk while peering into the deep pit and listens for the echoing cries of the kids.

The vice-principal, in the meanwhile, has called 911.

Now, they all arrive in the E.R.—children, police, teacher, vice-principal, medics, all in a flurry. A few of the "fallen" are walking, others are on stretchers. Doctors and nurses are in immediate attendance.

The vice-principal goes off to make the necessary calls—to the school, to parents. The teacher takes the uninjured remnants of the class back to school.

Fortunately, the worst injury is a broken ankle. The cast on that small leg will serve as a scroll for seven-year-old art and ribaldry, and make its wearer, the most injured one of the seven, the hero of the moment.

Not one child remains behind to be hospitalized. A lucky, lucky day.

■ ■ ■

The paramedic rushes through the doors, carrying a little girl about two. She is quiet, and nothing seems to be wrong with her, but the father, his face drawn with anxiety, is shouting, "She's taken my whole bottle of nitroglycerin pills. The ones I use for my heart condition. God help me, she's going to die!"

We whisk the child into the E.R., and while one doctor immediately begins to examine her, a pediatrician is rushing down the corridor.

The little girl fusses and whines, apparently startled and resentful of all the commotion around her. She clings to her mother, who is shaking uncontrollably, seeking protection against this unaccustomed attention.

After several hours of observation, the child's vital signs remain normal and there is a growing recognition that in no way has she been affected by ingesting the pills.

One of the nurses asks again, "How many pills were there in the bottle?"

The father still doesn't remember exactly. "But a lot . . . oh Jesus, a lot of them."

"She seems all right," the nurse reassures the parents. "Yes, she seems okay."

Calmer now, his relief heaved up in great sighs, the father reflects. "Well, maybe there weren't that many pills. Maybe I was wrong about that."

The child is fortunate. She is able to leave with her parents. "Keep out of the reach of children." Won't parents ever learn? This little girl is lucky—a fifteen-month-old baby we'd had in the E.R. some time earlier was not as fortunate. The child swallowed an entire bottle of liquid detergent. It was a touch-and-go moment; the doctors and nurses worked slavishly to save his life. They finally managed to detoxify him, but the trauma of the treatment and the long stay in the hospital that followed will not be without its psychological payments. The emotional cost of this kind of experience to child and parents is incalculable.

4 A RIDE IN THE AMBULANCE

Early on in my capacity as administrator, I felt the value of understanding every component, every factor, every nuance, every piece of every action that impacts on emergency services; to be in touch with the anxiety of a patient sitting in the sometimes endless wait of any E.R.—or the immediate anxiety of being rolled in on an ambulance gurney. The only way to accomplish this, I realized, was to take a vital part in all of these areas of my responsibility.

Budgets and paperwork and meetings and mandates, these alone would not do. It was necessary and important that I expose myself to the actual physical and emotional experience—to be a part of it.

To this end, in the week before my position became official, I decided that I would start to explore the waiting room. One afternoon, I entered, dressed in a hat and coat, feeling an imposter, though legitimately curious, and sat down on one of the waiting-room chairs.

In those few moments, sitting and waiting, I recognized the mandate the hospital had assigned when they asked me to assume this position. It was most complex and most important and I had made a solemn commitment to take it on. Every day I would remind my staff of the need to be

23

aware and duly compassionate in their behavior toward all patients.

Now I was "sitting in" on another aspect of my job. I had committed myself to ride in the ambulance with the night shift.

So here I was, bouncing along in the "bus," feeling a rush of adrenaline in my system.

Before too long, the value of this experience would be evident.

In New York City, any citizen who has a problem, whether it be medical, crime, or fire, calls 911. There, at a central unit, a battery of personnel funnels the calls in the appropriate directions. A worker connects the medical emergencies to EMS, the Emergency Medical Service. Hospital ambulances are connected to the EMS system, even though they are owned by the hospitals. The ambulance nearest to the address calling in the problem is assigned to take that call.

The information relayed over this radio is a constant stream of trouble: a miscarriage on the third floor of an office building; a child who misstepped on the bus and suffered a lacerated lip; a man stuck in an elevator; a stove explosion—bad facial burns; officer reported shot in subway—the reports go on and on. There is no end to them.

Then there are the numbers that are radioed through: 53—accident requiring an ambulance; 54—medical emergency also requiring an ambulance; 1030—a policeperson in trouble. We have, along with these references, our own name and code number for which to listen. Every hospital ambulance system does.

As is the custom at the change of every shift, the guys had, of course, checked the engine, changed the oil, and, with the scrupulous attention of engineers on the NASA program, made certain that "all systems were go." Since the ambulances are in use twenty-four hours every day, they must be properly attended. Any breakdown, where a life may be at stake and depends upon the speed of arrival, is of serious concern and can rest heavily upon the heart.

There is a minimum of space in the cab of the ambulance, just enough for one EMT or paramedic behind the wheel and the other crowded in next to him or her on the passenger seat—with barely any knee room. Every inch of space is utilized for the storage of equipment—lifesaving equipment: a gurney, oxygen tanks, I.V.'s, knee and leg braces, splints, bandages, blood-pressure gauges, mast trousers—inflatable trousers that provide pressure on the lower body to equalize the flow of blood, and keep the lower body immobilized. Everything has been planned to ameliorate trauma while a patient is being whisked from the original point of pickup to the E.R. setting.

The paramedics are highly skilled technicians capable of providing life-sustaining ventilatory assistance and cardiac massage, capable of monitoring and treating complex cardiac rhythms, capable of aiding the patients in many important ways. If specifically designed equipment and portable radio-telemetry devices are available, paramedics can provide care on the street or in an office or apartment— care that in earlier years could have been offered only in the most highly sophisticated of hospital settings. By transmitting cardiogram tracings and verbal reports to the physicians with whom they can be in constant contact (when the telemetry devices are in place), they can effectively extend the eyes and ears of the physicians into areas otherwise inaccessible, and they can initiate treatment several minutes sooner—minutes that may prove lifesaving.

There are two radios in the bus, both transmitting and receiving simultaneously, sending out a constant barrage of instructions. One is a walkie-talkie that is in direct communication with the police department; the other is a 911 radio receiving all the calls for emergencies.

There was not always the walkie-talkie. It was as a result

of this first experience on the ambulance that I convinced the hospital to make the walkie-talkie system available to all of the EMT's and paramedics.

When I first joined the department, a group of the guys had asked to meet with me. They were extremely upset. They talked of being called into some settings where, once having arrived, there was absolutely no way of making contact with anyone in the "outside world," and how frightening this was for them. They talked of places where even the police hesitated to enter but where their medical duty obliged them to go. They asked whether I would ride with them to see for myself what they repeatedly faced on their calls to houses or apartments in high-crime locales, sometimes to streets where every light had been deliberately blown out and where the particles of glass still littered the pavements.

I had promised I would ride with them. Now I sat peering out of the window. Suddenly, there was an urgent call: "Stabbing at One Hundred Twelfth Street, apartment seventy-one."

It was 1 A.M., a miserable foggy night with patches of rain hitting the streets and the pitch-dark overpowering, as we double-parked the ambulance in front of the given address. A few pedestrians, looming as dark splotches of shadow stood about, and as we moved to the back doors of the bus to fetch the gurney, the shadows seemed to move in closer, menacingly. Ignoring them, we entered the building and started to climb.

Number seventy-one in this crumbling relic of a tenement, whose prime was lived out at the turn of the century, meant no elevator. It also meant not one flight up, nor two, nor even three, but seven narrow flights of stairs, all malodorous and all in total darkness. One of the neighbors who had been waiting outside for us to arrive trailed the steps behind us, cursing under his breath and telling us there was no electricity in the entire building.

"Goddamn landlord shut it off months ago!"

Although our eyes had adjusted to the blackness and the eeriness of moving up the many stair landings in a totally unfamiliar and hostile environment—people occasionally opening their apartment doors as we trekked by, and blurting out obscenities to those "motherfuckers" in their building, stumbling over loose garbage and broken toys and splintered whiskey bottles—our nerves had not.

As we approached the seventh floor, now almost thoroughly winded, a voice screamed out, "In here, in here!"

We followed the voice and entered a room steeped in darkness; not a lit candle, only a tiny ribbon of light from someone holding a flashlight, the beam pointing to the floor. A body lay there, rocking from side to side and moaning softly.

Within this thin band of light, the guys bent down to take a look, and immediately they began their work to staunch the bleeding they could hardly see but could feel oozing out from somewhere. I could not determine where.

They worked in complete silence; even the moaning had stopped. Then, suddenly, I had the weirdest feeling. I knew there were two EMT's in the room; I knew there was someone holding the flashlight; I knew there was the victim of the stabbing lying stilled on the floor; I knew I was there. That made five of us.

Wrong!

Voices started to echo from parts of the room I could not define. There was no way in that blackness to discern whether we were in a small room or a large one. I heard at least three different male voices and the high soprano banshee wail of one female voice. An argument ensued and the voices rose from the deep silence that had existed when we first entered to a vulgar and vituperative crescendo of ear-shattering proportions; insult, anger, burgeoning threats—a rehashing, no doubt, of the violent expressions and emotions that had precipitated the stabbing.

Then we, the "saviors," became the target of their fury.

"Why the fuck ain't you doin' somethin'?"

"Why don't you move it and get him the hell outta here?"

"And after you fuckers get him out, you better keep your motherfuckin' mouths shut if you know what's good for ya."

My heart was pounding, my knees shaking; John and Ted were working swiftly and efficiently, lifting the victim onto the gurney. They had checked his vital signs and we were readying our exit.

One thought played leapfrog over my fright. Any one of us could have been attacked or brutally beaten here, and we would not even have known what our attackers looked like. There was no identification possible in the grimy blackness.

"Out. Let's get out of here," I prayed tonelessly.

A litany of loud vulgar curses pursued us to the door, but we were able to start the long trek down the stairs, again fighting the garbage and the toys and the broken bottles—and the dark.

This part of the journey, maneuvering down the seven flights took much longer than our trek up. The comfort of the patient, his weight, the size of the stretcher making the bends on the rickety stairs, and the awful dark made for a painfully slow trip down.

I heard a noise behind me (I was bringing up the rear, or down the rear, as it were). Something came rolling on the steps after us. I wasn't sure whether it was an article we had accidentally kicked into or whether someone had thrown whatever it was at us. I didn't care much at that point. I wanted out—out at least to the questionable safety of the street. Even the fog and the shadowy lolling pedestrians who had seemed so menacing earlier were a comfort.

And then we were back in the bus and racing to the hospital.

I asked the guys, "How can you keep so cool, keep on doing your job when . . ."

"Cool?" came back the reply. "Are you kidding? We

were scared shitless. It may not have shown, but scared shitless we were. Jeez! Unless we have a walkie-talkie that connects us with the police on the outside, we're gonna continue to be that scared on calls like this. You saw what it was like. Please . . . you gotta help us."

Damn tootin' I would.

Several weeks later, they had their walkie-talkies.

Not every experience in the ambulance is as grim and frightening as that night shift was. I recall a subsequent ride on the bus during an early evening shift. As we started out, a call came through on the radio.

"Yankee Twelve, heart attack, Central Park at Columbus Circle entrance."

The first call of *our* shift.

We had been "cruising," which meant that our bus was wandering the streets, ready for any action. At the moment of the call, we happened to be coasting through Central Park. It was not yet 5 P.M. Through the back window, I saw an old man walking his three dogs, barely able to keep up with their pace. I watched a large group of joggers doing their thing, and a few scurrying squirrels doing theirs. I had not been in Central Park for a long time, and it was both soothing and odd to be viewing it this way, seeing the budding scenery and the passing events through the window of an ambulance.

Then came the "Yankee Twelve, heart attack!"

On went the whirling lights, on went the siren, and off we went.

We were only seconds away from Columbus Circle. We arrived to find a cluster of people surrounding someone who lay on the cement near the entrance to the park. The paramedics on this shift, a man and woman, rushed over and the cluster parted. A middle-aged woman lay there.

"Oh, brother—it's Gertie!" The paramedic looked down at the woman, speaking in a tone of voice Laurence Olivier could not have improved upon, redolent as it was with a rising and falling cadence that managed to capture every nuance of surprise, irritation, pained recognition, and, finally, a humorous disgust. "Gertie!" he reiterated.

A grunt—from ground level.

"All right, Gertie, what's the problem this time? How come you didn't stay when we took you into the E.R. last evening?"

Up from the ground stared a blousy, boozy, disheveled caricature of a woman.

"I don't feel good," Gertie growled in a deep basso that had the raspiness of ground glass. "And you're no help. Take me to Bellevue."

"Gertie"—the reply was patience held together by a safety pin—"we are not a taxi service. Now get up and let's see what's happening this time."

"Jeez, I can't get up." The rasp became uglier and tougher. "I fell down."

"Gertie, are you drunk again?"

"You motherfucker, I ain't drunk. I just had a coupla nips. Take me to Bellevue, ya bastards. They'll let me sleep."

Several onlookers in the crowd could not understand the stern, rather cavalier attitude of the paramedics. One of the onlookers was becoming enraged. "That poor lady fell down! Why don't you take care of her? Obviously, she's had a heart attack."

He knew it.

But these particular paramedics and, for that matter, most of the E.R. staff knew differently. They knew Gertie better. She had an alcohol problem that she seemed to thoroughly enjoy, and she was in no way about to relinquish her pleasure in it to satisfy the standards of either the medical world or the world at large.

She just didn't like sleeping on the street.

What she wanted was a "bunk." So, when Gertie had tooted off a really strong one (which happened at least two or three evenings a week just at sunset), she had the inventiveness to create some kind of incident witnessed by onlookers who would call for an ambulance.

Dutifully, the bus would arrive and indeed transport Gertie to the hospital to be checked out—just in case there really was some kind of medical need, or just in case she *had* fallen down, or just in case.

At any rate, to the E.R., Gertie went.

She would be transferred to a stretcher and wheeled into a receiving cubicle, her vital signs taken by a nurse, and then she would be left to wait. Gertie was quite resourceful. She had figured out that this was the best way to get a room and bed and sack out. And if the E.R. was busy enough, which was almost always the case, and if she was not seen by the doctor for a long while, that is exactly what she would get—a comfortable snooze.

If, however, it was possible for a doctor to get to her quickly, she would become furious. This was not part of her plan. Out would pour a string of obscenities we could not even find in a pornographic lexicon (although we once tried). "You shithead motherfuckering cockblowers, you . . ." being the simplest, most understandable phrases.

Continuing her litany of filth, without even a pause for breath, and never once repeating a single phrase, she would, with an abusive glare at the staff, hop off the stretcher and stalk out.

This was the third time this week that the script had been replayed. The medics were not thrilled. Nevertheless, they encouraged Gertie to go to Roosevelt in the ambulance to be checked out again—just in case.

Gertie, however, was screaming for Bellevue, where they would "goddammit" let her sleep.

The concerned onlookers who had remained to see this vignette through, and who were still convinced that Gertie had truly had a heart attack, also encouraged her to go along with us. Finally, reluctantly, she offered a grunt of agreement but insisted she be carried the few feet to the ambulance. The paramedics got on each side of her, lifted her, and supported the flopping, sagging form into the back of the bus.

No sooner had she released her arms from around their necks than, with a practiced familiarity, she leaned over, took a pillow and a blanket from a neatly stacked pile, fluffed the pillow up, lay down, and tucked herself into the blanket, cocooning her body into total comfort.

"Uh-uh. No," our female paramedic said. "Get up. Come on, sit up. I'll sit with you. You can't go to sleep now. Wait till we get you to the hospital." She leaned over and propped Gertie into an upright position.

"Lousy motherfucking bitch." Gertie spat. "You can kiss my ass."

Out she jumped from the ambulance and stomped down the park path.

The onlookers, who by this time had started on their way, having seen Gertie safely ensconced in the van, were now no more than miniature figures in the distance.

Despite this, in a fit of pique and frustration, the paramedic opened the van door and bellowed into the wind, "Take a good look. There goes your heart attack!"

During the preceding urban comedy that was being played out, I had remained on the sidelines observing, but I soon became aware that *I* was being observed.

A young man, a hippie prototype—tight jeans and leather headband—sauntered through the group until he stood directly in front of me, blocking my way.

"Hey lady," he said, his T-shirt revealing powerful muscles, which he kept flexing automatically, on his face a half-smile. "Hey, you from da hospital?"

"Mmmmm," I replied.

"I'm from da Bronx. I need help."

From the Bronx. No need to declare that.

"Hey lady, ya see, I got this problem. Can you help?"

"The hospital is only two blocks that way," I said politely, pointing west.

"Nah . . . I want you to drive me."

"I'm sorry, but we can't do that. But if you need help, by all means go over to the Emergency Room."

He stood a moment in concentrated thought.

"Nah, I guess I won't bother if you won't drive me there. Ya see . . . I came into da Big Apple ta deal some drugs here in Central Park. Guess I'll take care of my hernia some udder time. T'anks anyway."

And raising a grimy-fingered salute, he sauntered away.

Almost immediately after we got ourselves settled back into the bus, another urgent request came booming out over the radio.

"Yankee Twelve—boy hit by car, One Hundred Sixth and Broadway. Yankee Twelve."

We took off and out of the park, our siren screeching and lights twirling, and hightailed it up Broadway.

As we shot through the streets, it was amazing to consider the variety of responses from both pedestrians and drivers to our "Angel of Mercy." The long whine of the siren and the oncoming lights were usually enough to command attention and elicit the response we demanded.

Out of the way, dammit, out of the way, the siren screamed.

In most cases, this demand was respected—but not always. Some drivers get confused and do the wrong thing; they keep moving and do not pull over to let the bus pass. Others will attempt to pull around to the left of the vehicle (a most dangerous decision), a possibility of which medics must constantly be alert. Still others egocentrically just go on with their business as usual, getting in and out of cabs or paying their fares, making no attempt to hurry things along, despite the frantic tooting of our horn, despite the twirling lights. And in this mechanized world, there are those people in cars or walking or cycling or roller-skating with their earphones on, music blasting away, making them oblivious to everything but their private world of sound.

Driving the ambulance is a dangerous art. It always has been.

Inconceivable though it would seem to us today, there was an extended period when *no* ambulance service was offered by any of the hospitals—and this was mainly because of the tragedies that had been brought on by the need for speed.

Originally, for the first six years of Roosevelt's existence—from 1871 to 1877—patients were brought into the hospital on horseback or in private carriages by relatives or friends, or, in the case of accident, by the police. There were no regulations, and patients were taken to one hospital or another at random. A contemporary report indicated that too often the police would carry their patients to hospitals that were more distant than necessary. In 1877, the city government, therefore, established ambulance "districts"; the Roosevelt district embraced a major portion of Manhattan.

On September 10, 1877, the very first ambulance service went into effect.

The vehicle was a cumbersome one—horse-drawn, it more closely resembled a modern-day hearse than a lifesaving bus. (It is amusing to note that in its first year of service, the cost of upkeep, feed, and stabling amounted to $205.19 and this was considered something of a drain on the hospital's finances. Ah, for the good old days.)

Dr. J. West Roosevelt, in an article published by *Scribner's Magazine* in those early years, described the ambulance service of that time most graphically: "The ambulance was summoned by telegraph, the horse led into the shafts and immediately secured by a drop harness." Out of the shed it would gallop, with a driver hanging on to the reins and the traditionally peak-capped intern riding in back.

In what became a disastrous experiment (responding perhaps to the call for progress in the new century), the horse-drawn vans in 1900 were replaced by electric buses, but this lasted only three years. "These electric cars proved too undependable, too expensive, and too liable to mechanical failure." So, in 1903, the stables were opened again, the horses groomed, and the electric vans put out to pasture in a faraway barn.

As time went on, however, even those horse-drawn vans became too expensive, and a formal request for financial aid from the city to support this service was rejected. The basic reason for this refusal was the "item of cost" interestingly enough, which arose from the breakneck driving that characterized the service in those days. Numberless tragedies took place on the streets, and the hospital budget soon was being eroded by claims for over a hundred thousand dollars, claims made by people injured or killed by the wildly galloping horses as they raced to or from the hospital.

In December of 1908, the trustees of Roosevelt Hospital voted to abandon ambulance service altogether. It was not reinstated until six years later, in 1914.

During those six years, the now decrepit vehicle, denuded of its warning gong and drawn by a mangy ancient horse, was used only to transfer alcoholic and psychiatric patients from Roosevelt to Bellevue. In this function, the van filled with its boisterous and rowdy load and the sole embarrassed intern riding in the rear, moving slowly across town, was a familiar sight.

Yes, I thought as we whizzed past candy shops and delicatessens and restaurants, up Broadway, weaving in and out of the many buses, trucks, cars, taxis, and bicycles, driving the ambulance is a dangerous art and our drivers must be

.particularly skilled to survive. It is also why, despite the urgency of many situations, the driver will always brake momentarily at cross streets, so that the ambulance crew themselves do not end up as casualties.

Through the fray, I hung on tightly to my seat as we 'Yankee 12'd' to the scene of the accident.

A little boy of about five lay on the pavement. A woman, obviously his mother, knelt at his side, holding his hand in hers, weeping and murmuring, "It's going to be all right, Davey. It's going to be all right."

Standing nearby was a slightly older boy of about eight who was moving around and around in narrow circles as though circumferencing a Frisbee, and wringing his small hands. A few feet away, a police officer was questioning a young man who leaned against the side of his car trembling and crying.

"He just darted out in front of me," he kept repeating, snuffling away his tears. "He just darted out and I couldn't stop in time."

His story seemed to check out. The older boy said that he and his little brother were going across the street to a candy store and the little boy broke away and ran into the gutter and then . . .

Fortunately, the car had been going at a relatively slow speed—ten miles an hour—because the driver had been looking for a place to park. The impact on the child was, therefore, not as serious as it might have been. The medics took the vital signs while asking the mother some basic questions about the boy's medical history. They also wanted to know how he had been carried from the street to the sidewalk.

The woman, distraught and shaking but desperately trying for control, answered that she had heard the screeching of the brakes. "I ran to the window—we're on the second floor—I saw what happened. Oh God! I rushed down to the street and lifted my baby up and just . . . just carried him here . . . I wanted to get him out of the way of the traffic. My baby.''

The child was conscious but seemed stunned and complained quietly of pain in his back. Out came the gurney. He was lifted carefully onto it and settled into the back of the bus. Mother and older brother joined me there. One of the medics sat at the youngster's head, observing him and making him as comfortable as possible as we started for the E.R.

I looked at the child, covered from toe to chin with a thin blanket to keep him warm; he was staring with frightened eyes along the length of the ceiling and walls, reacting to the awesome equipment attached to and hanging from the different sections of the interior. He once locked eyes with his mom, just to be sure that she was still there.

Mom was bravely keeping her composure. She sat with her arms around the older boy, who was still trembling and who kept muttering in a small voice, "It's my fault. I should have watched him better. It's all my fault.''

"No . . . no. You mustn't think that. Ever. You hear me.'' She squeezed his hands consolingly. Then, with lips tightly pursed and a turn of her head to look him directly in the eye, she whispered, "He was . . . was a very bad boy to run off like that. That's all.''

Seemingly reassured, the boy whispered back, "Is he going to be all right, Mom?''

It was painful to watch the strained maneuvering of the mother, fearful for the young one and equally fearful of the effects of this trauma upon the older boy.

"Yes . . . yes, he's going to be okay. You wait and see.''

We took the youngster to the nearest hospital, which has a small pediatric emergency unit, and delivered him to the care of the waiting professionals.

Our task was completed.

■   ■   ■

Hopping back into the bus, the medics called 911 to inform them that there had been "closure" (meaning that the patient was now in the care of a hospital) and they, therefore, were once again ready for action, this all being part of the 911 procedures.

Down Broadway we cruised, past the strip of stores. One of the medics remembered that there was a favorite pizza shop along the way. We were all tired and hungry and we decided to make a pit stop to pick up some food. As always, one of the team stayed with the bus to listen for calls. The radio is never left unmonitored, with the exception of those rare times when a call might go in to 911 to ask for permission to take a ten-minute necessity break; or, of course, when the crew is on a call.

So we had a break—snacking away on pizza and slurping our sodas out of cans. Well, the cheese is protein, I thought. It'll give us energy and a bit of a boost.

I kept my ears tuned to the various calls coming through to all of the ambulances throughout the city. In a city the size of New York, in a borough the size of Manhattan, there would forever be the need of those in trouble for help from those waiting to administer it.

"Unconscious male on street at Forty-eighth between Broadway and Seventh." "Female with chest pains at corner of Tenth and Seventy-fourth." "VDP in synagod at Twelfth and Fifty-first Street."

"What," I asked, "is a VDP? And did I hear right? What the heck is a synagod?"

The guys laughed. Apparently, this particular individual on the 911 line was notable for the number of malapropisms she regularly sprayed across the airwaves on her shift. It was no joke. Simply her way of "hearing the world."

Oh well, a synagogue was certainly an appropriate place to encompass a synagod.

"And a VDP?"

"A very disturbed person."

As we looked out of the window at the passing scene on Broadway, nibbling our pizzas and watching the stream of humanity go by, one of the medics said, "Hey, look!"

Parading down the street was a very tall person wearing gold boots with tan army pants tucked into them so that they puffed out at the thighs, a purple satin blouse opened down to the navel, revealing several dozen gold and silver chains of various lengths, and with a frizzed-out hairdo that boasted a number of multicolored feathers pointing out in all directions from the scalp. A drum was slung over his?/her? neck.

"That my friend," the medic addressed me, "is a VDP!"

Well, now I knew. I was a fast study.

As we continued to cruise, the litany of woes coming across the two communication systems superimposed itself upon the noisy, colorful avenue sounds. A policeman on foot smiled and saluted us as we drove by.

"Hi, Joe," responded the medic sitting next to the driver.

We were approaching a red light and, parallel to our van, there, for all to see, was a small car with two grown men lying across the hood, traveling about twenty miles per hour; two other people besides the driver were inside the car.

Gads. A car in motion with three people inside and two people on its roof, traveling twenty miles an hour in midtown Manhattan.

Crazy!

One of the medics leaned out of his window as we halted for the light. "Shall we wait for you fellows?" he asked. "You're certainly gonna need us sooner or later!"

"Yankee Twelve . . . cardiac arrest at Mal's restaurant." Cardiac arrest! No time to lose.

Out of the way, I was silently screaming to the cars in

front. Come on, get out of our way. Dammit. Fast. It might be *you* we're rushing to next time!

The West Side restaurant toward which we were speeding was not unfamiliar to me. I had eaten there several times. It was close to the hospital and close to where I lived. A small intimate place, it was situated within the theater district and was well frequented, for it had a reputation for serving excellent Italian food.

As one entered, there was a long bar area to one side and beyond that, a squared-off room for serious dining, which held about ten tables. It was early—the dinner hour was just beginning. Most of the diners, recently seated, had gotten up from their tables and were huddled near the bar area, watching.

The ambulance crew had rushed in, only to find a second set of medics who had arrived minutes earlier. Now the four of them were crouched down, making a vigorous effort to resuscitate a middle-aged gentleman who lay on the floor in front of the row of bar stools. They kept checking his vital signs, and implementing one indicated procedure after another. A call was made to a base station to check with a doctor at the other end for information and advice on further appropriate medical procedures, since what they were working at so feverishly was failing. *Had* failed. And yet . . .

I stood in the entranceway watching the activity and feeling once again with a sharp stinging acuity the slim line that exists between life and death.

A man in his late fifties paced in circles nearby, talking agitatedly to no one in particular and listened to by no one, addressing the air in deep puzzlement and awe. "Jesus. We were just having a drink at the bar . . . getting ready for a good meal . . . lobster fra diavolo, he wanted. Lobster. Imagine." He punched a fist into the palm of his hand. "He was doing a card trick . . . and right then he . . . Jesus. He just retired last month. What am I going to tell his wife?"

The babble of words stopped. The pacing stopped. He

turned to me and withdrew a small brown bottle from his jacket pocket.

"See," he said, as though trying to indoctrinate me, "this is what keeps me going. The damned job with its pressures, it's a killer. This Librium—this is what keeps *me* from having a heart attack."

Having made this declaration, he turned to address the air again. "Jesus . . . what am I going to tell her?"

In the midst of all of this commotion, while the waiters dressed in their identical and sedate costumes stood against the walls, unmoving, and the bartender leaned over the bar absentmindedly polishing one glass over and over, his eyes glued to the frenzied effort taking place on the floor a startling sound pierced through the room: the sound of a woman's lilting laughter.

I looked up. There, toward the back of the dining area, in the exact center of my line of vision, sat a couple—a young woman and man, leaning in toward each other whispering, drinking their wine, totally unconcerned about what was taking place just a few feet away from them.

The images of the forever-stilled, graying face of the man on the floor, the anguished frustration of the medics laboring away, the puzzled and helpless pacing of the friend, superimposed upon a flash of teeth caught in open-mouthed laughter will be etched forever in my memory. Fellini himself could not have orchestrated a more bizarre scene.

Our medics' job was done. It was decided that the first medic team would take care of all the remaining details. The equipment was gathered and we moved back to our parked bus.

No time to speculate further, for no sooner had we pulled away from the curb than our code call blasted through the airwaves.

"Yankee Twelve . . . Yankee Twelve . . . woman injured on Riverside Drive."

And off we raced.

• • •

We arrived a few minutes later at the canopy of an old rococo apartment building. The doorman waved us in and as we walked through the wrought-iron doors into the lobby, ornate with its marble floor and now-faded golden cherubs smiling down from the ceiling and a large, somewhat dilapidated chandelier from which several crystal pieces were missing, we saw a little woman seated on a leather chair in a hunched-over position.

"Oh," she said, recognizing who we were, "oh, I'm sorry you were called. I don't need you. Thanks just the same."

"Wait now, Mrs. Liam," said the doorman. "Let them check you out. After all, you *were* knocked down."

"Really, I'm all right," she insisted. "Listen, my parents are expecting me upstairs. They'll be worried."

Her parents? The woman before us was gray-haired and wrinkled and had reached the grand old age of seventy—at least. And her *parents* were expecting her?

"Yes, yes," she explained. "Momma and Poppa live with me. I went to visit a friend and they'll be very worried if I don't go back upstairs."

She went on to tell us that she was on her way home and was coming down her own block when a figure lurched out of the shadows and with one swift movement grabbed her purse and pushed her backward. She fell sideways onto the cement, her right hip taking the brunt of the fall.

A policeman already summoned to the lobby could get no identifying information about her assailant. She had not seen him; it was too dark and she was too numbed with fright.

"Well," said the cop, "this is one of the worst blocks in Manhattan for muggings."

Surprised, I said, "But this is one of the fancy neighborhoods—well patrolled."

"Fancy, schmancy," said he, "it's a dark street adjacent to the park. A perfect combination. Ideal to hide and wait to stalk a victim until the right moment—then, an easy

getaway into the park afterward. It's too bad. [...]
third mugging on this street this week. And w[...]
around, too."

The medics spoke gently to this elderly, vulnerable lady, all the while taking her vital signs and trying to convince her to come with us to be X-rayed—she might have broken her hip. At first she was adamant in her refusal. But when she tried to stand to prove to us that she was just badly shaken and superficially bruised, it brought such a cry of pain that she realized the wisdom of going to the hospital for further examination.

"Don't tell my parents," she pleaded with the doorman, "they cannot take any excitement. Anyway, I'm sure that after the X rays I'll be able to come back home tonight."

"Don't worry, Mrs. Liam, I won't tell them. I'll think of something."

The medics left and returned with a gurney and, very carefully, lifted one of the city's many mugging victims.

"I always keep my keys and some money in my coat pocket. This isn't the first time I've been mugged," she said. "But why, why?" She shook her head ruefully. "He had already grabbed my purse. Why didn't he just run away then? Do I look like an Olympic jogger who would chase him? Why did he have to knock me down and hurt me?"

"I wish I could answer that question," replied one of the medics.

It was just midnight when the van pulled into the ambulance courtyard of the hospital. I lumbered out of the back of the bus and took my leave with a wave of the hand and a "thanks, fellas" and began my trek home, emotionally and physically exhausted.

Hundreds of thoughts played through my head. I thought of the sweet face of the woman who had been mugged, and then of my own mother living alone and vulnerable to the mean and dangerous "big city" crimes. I reviewed the past hours and reflected that almost every case we attended might have been someone I knew, someone I loved, someone whom disaster hit.

Well, I could at least have a moment of pride and joy that in *my* tiny corner, in the orbit of my function, I was helping to ameliorate some of the troubles. And honing in still further—each time the ambulance went out on a call—our people were helping to better some of the problems.

And thinking this, I suddenly grew angry.

The medics had told me that 33 percent of all the calls to which they respond are unfounded, unnecessary, and ultimately a waste of time. They are grievous examples of the misuse of the ambulance system in our city.

Some regard the ambulance as a taxi service! Can you imagine the chutzpah, the audacity of people putting in an emergency call simply because they do not want to pay a cab for a ride to a hospital clinic appointment? They feign an illness or invent an accident, call 911 (an office that must take all calls seriously and cannot afford to make generalized judgments), and get their free ride.

Then there are those who become panic-stricken in an easily handleable situation, call for the ambulance, and, by the time it arrives, are waiting at the door with a shame-faced apology—"It's okay, we put a Band-Aid on the kid's elbow and it stopped bleeding, sorry, thanks anyway."

Worst of all, however, are those cases where no one is at the receiving end—prank calls. Prank calls that may cost the life of another human being.

Of the 67 percent of calls remaining, at least half, while honestly needing ambulance transport, do not need the advanced life-support systems that the paramedics are qualified and prepared to offer. Only one in every four cases that the paramedic unit attends actually has an appropriate need for the unit.

Hour after hour, day after day, we see the ambulances cruising our streets, and it is a comfort to know that if there is a need, it will be answered.

A great comfort.

TWENTY-FOUR HOURS A DAY . . .

A busload of junior-high-school kids draws up and parks right in front of the ambulance courtyard. The doors open and out struggles a mature man attempting to support the weight of a youngster whose body is buckling under him and practically begging to rest on the pavement. The thirteen-year-old is drunk, falling down, putty-kneed, noisily, happily drunk!

I hear the details while the young man is being examined: a plot, hatched for this day's class outing to the Museum of Natural History, a bottle sneaked out of the family liquor cabinet; the braggadocio of an adolescent male, wanting to strut before a desired, if unobtainable, girlfriend; a long, very long ride between Suffolk County and Manhattan during the morning rush hour, time enough to finish off a whole quart; a stewed-to-the-gills student and an extremely apprehensive teacher who had ordered the driver to pull into the nearest hospital—and who, at this moment, is faced with an overwhelming decision.

How can he best meet his responsibilities?

Take the rest of the students to the museum as was intended? Or wait out the sleep that the doctor recommends for the young man. Go or stay?

Obviously our young man does not need a visit to the

47

museum to see skeletons or spiders or dinosaurs. He is cheerfully creating them all out of his drunken self.

A long studied moment passes. The teacher finally makes his choice. The busload of students will simply wait for a few hours, eat the lunches they brought along, and play—Ghost? Twenty Questions?—well, play whatever games can be played on a bus.

"Whatever I can damn well think up and I can't think up much right now"—he turns to me and smiles wryly—"to entertain and subdue twenty-seven teenagers!" A shake of his head. "Yes, I think this is the best way. To wait. I'd be too worried about *that* one in there. Well"—he turned to go—"wish me luck!"

■ ■ ■

Several hours later, as I go through the E.R., I see the teacher and his shaky young patient exiting the door.

"I guess," I remark to the registrar, "that that young man's parents won't be too thrilled to pay this bill when it comes."

"Oh jeez!" The registrar reacts sharply. "It was so hectic all day, people coming in all the time, and that kid not able to stand or sit—he nearly toppled over—he was taken into the room immediately—jeez, I forgot to get the information."

"What!" I exclaim. I know how important it is for the hospital to be reimbursed for its services.

I dash through the waiting room, out the front door, and down to the curb just as the bus is pulling away.

"Wait!" I holler at the top of my lungs over the din of New York City traffic. "Wait!"

The bus rolls to a halt halfway down the street and I jog to catch up with it.

The door flings open and I board, huffing and puffing. "I'm sorry to hold you up," I say to the teacher, "but the registrar forgot to take the appropriate information on your student and we do need it so that the hospital can send a bill for services. I'm sure the family would want to pay for the examination and careful observation we offered for the past five hours, aren't you?"

"Of course," the teacher replies. "Let me write it down for you."

He pulls a pad and pencil out of his inner jacket pocket, turns to the young man who has been somehow sobered by my last statement, and says, "Give me your exact address and zip code for the lady."

The young man looks up sheepishly at first, then heaves a deep sigh, aware all of a sudden of the glowering resentment of his classmates for the long delay, and aware, too, that a moment of reckoning is sure to come.

He answers.

"Doghouse, U.S.A."

■ ■ ■

The door is flung open, then banged shut.

In they come, this man and woman, both in their early forties, staggering, reeling, barely able to stand.

By the time they reach the reception window, it is not difficult to understand that their major problem (and ours) is the levels of alcohol in their respective bloodstreams.

The ruckus they are creating is almost too much to bear on this hot, sticky, crowded, and chaotic Saturday night. We are all overworked and overtired. These two are neither aware nor concerned. They are both angry. The woman's face is badly bruised and there is a deep gash on the side of her upper right arm.

"Goddamn it," she says, seeming to address the startled waiting patients and their families rather than the object of her wrath. "Goddamn it, why did you have to hit me so hard!"

Her partner does not seem to appreciate this public display of his guilt, his responsibility for the gash.

"Shut up, you bitch," he replies.

Without consultation, the staff silently agrees that, for the good of the patients and everyone else, these two must be separated as rapidly as possible. After a quick run-through of the details for registration, the nurse is able to escort the woman into a free cubicle, where she is to wait for treatment. Her companion is asked to remain in the outer waiting room.

He begins to pace the small area, puffing away on one cigarette after another, inhaling a few times, then stamping out the rest on the floor, grinding the paper into crumbs with force. He is punishing the very tobacco upon which he depends.

Fifteen minutes later, the man storms up to the registrar and demands to know why his "lady" has not been treated and released and "what the hell is taking so long?"

First the clerk, then the nurse go to great pains to explain that this is a busy Saturday night, an especially busy time; his "lady" will certainly be attended to just as soon as possible.

The man grumbles and flops into a chair.

Another short period passes, evidently an interminable, unendurable stretch of minutes for this hyped-up, agitated, angry man. He rises and without much ado picks up his chair and sends it hurtling across the room, smashing into the door separating the waiting room from the inner cubicles.

Immediately, the security guard appears. All eyes are now focused upon the two men. Fury and excitement are rustling through the air, sending out vibrations that everyone can experience. A Roman circus threatens. Will the guard subdue the man? Will he arrest him? Will there be bloodshed?

A disappointment. The guard, after staring at this troublemaking culprit for a moment, picks up the chair, places it back in its original position, and quietly suggests to the man that he calm down at once or leave.

Then . . . things heat up again. For instead of taking his seat quietly, the man pushes past the guard and thrusts himself through the door to the "inner sanctum," shouting at the top of his lungs, "Where are you, honey? What have they done to you?"

The guard, in hot pursuit, grabs the man from behind as he is barreling down the main corridor of the E.R. A nurse picks up the phone and calls for security backup from another part of the hospital. The "lady" rushes out of her room and up to the security guard, who, by this time, has halted her wild man's projectory. She starts to beat at the guard, on his face and back, screaming all the while, "Let go of my man, you bastard! What are you doing to my man?"

Attracted by the tumult, a policeman awaiting treatment for a foot injury incurred that night in the line of duty hobbles barefoot out of *his* cubicle. At this very moment, a second security guard appears on the scene. What follows is a comic opera melee.

The woman is being restrained by the first guard while the police officer and a second guard are struggling to hold on to the man. All are in motion and shouting indecipherable phrases.

Finally, the man stops screaming, cursing, and flailing. Finally, the woman stops bludgeoning the guard with her fists and the policeman hobbles back into his room. Finally, slowly, the security guard releases his hold on the woman and the man shakes off his captor. Everyone just stands there.

Then in a blurred gravelly growl, the man turns to the woman and says, "Let's get out of this joint, honey. They ain't gonna help you. *I'll* help you."

In an equally gravelly basso, she answers, "Okay sweetie, I know you didn't mean to hurt me. Who needs these assholes, anyway?"

Arm in arm, they swagger down the hallway to the exit door.

"Wait!" huffs the nurse as she runs after them. "Wait, you shouldn't leave. You need to have your injury looked at."

"Forget it sister. Just forget it."

"Then," says the nurse, paying desperate attention to hospital protocol, "you've got to sign your E.R. sheet where it says 'refuses medical treatment.' "

She holds out the record sheet to the woman.

"Sign your E.R. sheet? Stick it up your ass."

• • •

There may be fancier, more scientific names—genetic predisposition, the disease of alcoholism. The sociologists and psychologists may offer us explanation and motivation—but whatever the causes, whatever the language, it alters neither the alcoholic's image nor the profound need for help.

UNFORTUNATES

During the day, they wander the nearby streets. They scrounge around the dumps and garbage pickup points; dirty torn article by article, they amass their household goods: old mattresses, broken-down parts of cots, clothes, brown paper bags filled with discarded decaying food—their basic necessities for survival. These they hide in alleyways, in the little nooks and crannies between the buildings that line the street across from the hospital.

When night falls and the world retires, when most of the city returns to the individual nonworking parts of their lives, the bums surreptitiously drag out their bits of "home"—their mattresses and bags and shreds of blanket—and settle themselves across from the hospital over some hot-air vents.

Then the drinking begins. A drunk, solitary or surrounded by a cluster of lolling, muttering cronies, leans against the stone bulwark of brick—and drinks.

Before the night is over, one or more of the drunken, disorderly derelicts will reel into our E.R. Beaten up, cut up, faces black and blue, broken-nosed and bloody—in they stagger. They need help.

Sometimes, when no fight has been precipitated and they are in a rowdy mood, they come into the E.R. on the hunt for trouble. After all, when one carries an unconscious quantum of rage and hostility and there's no one right at hand on whom to vent it in the middle of the night, when one's companions have already conked out on the sidewalk or wandered off to pick up another sweet dream in a bottle, one must seek out a psychological battlefield: the Emergency Room. Companion or antagonist, it is always there.

■ ■ ■

An alcoholic, filthy, his clothes rotting on his back, enters the Emergency Room in a drunken state. We've seen him many times before. He is a regular, a part of the life of our hospital. He swaggers belligerently into our E.R. every so often for various needs to be filled, none of which have anything to do with obtaining medical attention.

Today, he storms in and says he has a sore throat and must be seen immediately. We register him and ask him to have a seat; we have some very serious cases to look after at the moment. He sits down on the plastic chair. The waiting patients surrounding him edge to the side just a little in an attempt to escape his malodorousness.

He is no sooner seated than he jumps up, waves his arms, shouts rowdily, and almost topples into the lap of a pregnant woman.

Jean Adams is on duty tonight, and Jean knows this

"patient" from many encounters. She decides she had better get him out of the way. Luckily, one of the examining rooms is free and Jean leads him muttering and stumbling to wait his turn there.

"Goddamn! I've got to see the doc immediately," he bellows, enraged. He has "important business" and can't waste his fuckin' time hanging around.

Jean has a good idea what that "important business" is; even *where* it is. The Bar, a local watering hole, is the "boardroom" for "business men" of this kind. It is open day and night and we frequently get the spillover, especially on Saturday nights.

Jean is just as anxious to get him out in a hurry as he is to go. She assures the angry, staggering man that she'll try to round up a doctor to examine him as quickly as possible, but she must get on with her work. He is irate. He utters slurred curses at all and sundry. Nurse Adams leaves the room.

There is a long moment of silence. Then, suddenly from within that room comes a ripping, tinny, tearing noise. Jean rushes back in.

There stands her inebriated patient near the far end of the room. The sink, which just moments before had been mounted on the wall, is now cradled in the drunk's arms. A stream of water pours forth from the wall.

Defeated, Jean mutters feebly, "Is there a plumber in the house?"

■ ■ ■

If an octopus came ambling along Broadway dressed in a tuxedo with patent leather dancing slippers on each of his eight tentacles, I doubt there would be one raised eyebrow.

Going into the registrar's area of the E.R., I see a well-dressed, rather bleary-eyed woman sauntering up to the clerk.

"Can I help you?" the clerk asks.

In a pleasant tone, the woman responds, "Yes." Then, matter-of-factly, as though displaying a cut made with a paring knife while preparing a chicken dinner for a neat little bourgeois family, she pulls back the loose sleeve of her dress and continues. "I was shooting up and the needle broke off."

And, holding up her arm and shoving it almost into the clerk's face, she points with the index finger of her other hand. "Here, look."

An inch of needle juts out from a vein.

The clerk, without the least flicker of changed expression, of surprise or condemnation, replies, "Certainly, we'll be happy to help you. Can I have your Blue Cross/Blue Shield number? Name? Address, please?"

• • •

A young woman, supported by a man holding her around her waist, staggers into the E.R. The woman is hurriedly pressed into a chair by the man, who then moves quickly to the registrar's desk. "That lady over there took something," he says hastily. "She may be overdosed."

Before the clerk can gather any more information, the man beats a hasty retreat out the door just as Amy and a security officer enter the waiting area. They get the woman into a room and onto a stretcher. Her pupils are wildly dialated; she is hyperventilating.

His amateur diagnosis was on target. She's obviously overdosed. Had he watched that dose go in?

We have to work quickly. Her stomach is pumped.

We see from some papers on her person that she is from outside the country. She is not a resident in the United States. We call the embassy of her country, give them her name and the few details we know, and plead for help in locating her family. The representatives at the embassy are hesitant, reluctant, and, in fact, cooly respond that there is nothing they can do to help.

It is all perplexing and strange. For the moment, we are impotent.

When finally she becomes cogent, her condition stabilized, she wants to know where she is. We tell her. She appears stunned. She is surprised to be in a hospital. But much stranger is her reaction to being in the United States. She just does not know how she got to this country.

The last thing she remembers was being in Singapore. So how can she be here now? Her confusion appears genuine. We call her home overseas. We are able to reach her father. His shock is also apparent. He tells us she left for work that morning and did not arrive home in the evening. The family was not too worried but had begun looking for her. The father cannot adjust to what he is hearing. America? The United States? Impossible!

She was dismissed late that evening as medically cleared. And yet . . .

I still wonder about this young woman. Kidnapping? Drug smuggling? Intended rape and forced prostitution? And what happened to her? We will never know.

5 ST. PATRICK'S DAY

"I tell you, one kid, stewed out of his skull, was trying to climb up the fifty-foot flagpole in the Wollman Memorial Skating Rink. That little SOB could've killed himself. And those mobs of kids scrambling over the rocks and literally rolling all over those hills in Central Park were looking up at him, waving their hands, thumbs up and screaming, 'Go-go, go on—make it!' They egged him on, encouraging him, so mob-psyched that they couldn't recognize the danger; they were jostling a policeman who was trying to use his walkie-talkie to get reinforcements. They just didn't give a damn, I tell you. It was like being in a zoo."

The reporter from one of New York's leading newspapers had come to interview me. It was a few minutes before noon. It was apparent that he was truly shocked and needed time and space to decompress from the experience outside. He couldn't seem to stop talking.

"I could hardly make it into the park—the streets are so packed. And coming up the Avenue of the Americas"—he shook his head in disbelief—"it isn't even lunchtime yet and the place looks as though a cyclone of garbage swept through it. Thousands of candy wrappers and crumpled paper bags and decaying food and even some clothes—littering the streets—it felt ankle-deep. And those youngsters, rowdying eight abreast across the sidewalks so you had to step into the gutter to get around them. They were swaggering with their six-packs of beer, swizzling, guzzling hard liquor out of fifths half-hidden in paper bags—openly, although it is absolutely against the law. And the police—mostly just ignoring the violation." He took a breath. "Reminded me of Alice in Wonderland. You know—'The Walrus and the Carpenter.'" He began to recite:

> *"If seven maids with seven mops*
> *Swept it for half a year,*
> *Do you suppose," the Walrus said,*
> *"That they could get it clear?"*

I picked up the lines, "'I doubt it,' said the Carpenter, and shed a bitter tear.'"

"I doubt it, too," the reporter declared emphatically. And it's the same everywhere. Even in the park—well, anyway, about that kid on the flagpole"—he picked up the almost forgotten thread—"unbelievable! When he finally did make it to the top and was hanging on to the huge gold ball there, gyrating and making faces and clowning for the benefit of his audience, the kids down below started to pound each other on their backs and horse around and swill more beer, shooting streamers of foam into the air, shouting their congratulations.

"They were squashing and smashing those beer cans and liquor bottles and throwing them around on the grass and at passersby and at one another—and *throwing up* all over the place. These were babies—teens and even younger. I tell you, it's a scene you wouldn't believe!"

Oh, yes I would, I thought. "I know. I've been this route before. Dozens of them will be arriving at our doors pretty soon. They usually begin piling in about midafternoon when all the stuff they've been on starts to take its toll."

"What's it like here?" the reporter asked. "As bad as the street?"

"Worse. They can be mighty sick by the time they get here. There'll be troops of them, some wheeled in, some carried in by friends, some staggering in on their own last bit of steam. But we're prepared for it. There are extra stretchers kept ready in the halls, extra nurses have been added to the shift, doctors all through the hospital are at the ready.

"You know, I'd bet that if you asked a hundred people what day they think would be the busiest, the craziest time in the E.R., most of them would answer New Year's Eve or maybe July Fourth. Drinking and accidents on the road for New Year's, firecrackers for the Fourth. Not so. The roughest time we have is today, St. Patrick's Day. This one's a real mess. The walking wounded are due soon, the ones with cuts and bruises and fractures from fights and falls. Those are the easy cases. Most of them will be treated and released today. Their parents will come to pick them up, they'll be embarrassed and apologetic. That is, some of them. That is, until next year. Those are the easy ones. The others—well, with the combination of drugs and alcohol, the results aren't pretty."

I interrupted myself when I heard the ambulance doors fly open. That was the end of the interview.

Being wheeled by the paramedics on a stretcher into the hallway was a young girl. She was writhing and moaning. The medics were whispering to her, trying to soothe and calm her, but the effect was just the opposite. Her moans became screams, perhaps because she dimly recognized that she was in a hospital. She was obviously terrified. Several nurses and doctors converged around the stretcher. An I.V. was set up immediately while her vital signs were taken. They tried to evaluate how out of it she was by her responses to routine questions: "What's your name? Do you know your name? How old are you? Were you with anyone before you were brought here? Is there someone you'd like us to call for you?"

The screaming continued, breaking off at moments into

a low animal whimpering, followed then by wails and gib-berish. We all could tell that it would be many hours before she would be able to give us any information that might be helpful in contacting her family, and certainly she was in no condition to tell us what she had ingested that had brought her to this pitiable state.

Lily Boland, one of the doctors on duty, examined her. All she could learn was that whatever drug or drugs the girl had taken, she was overdosed. We could lose her. Pumping her stomach was necessary—and fast. A team went into action.

This would be only one of the many cases I would be monitoring throughout the afternoon. My job was to go into the room from time to time, question the patient again and again, trying to learn the name of someone to call, or at least some clue so that eventually I'd find a parent or relative. Then, as gently as possible, I'd let them know that someone they cared about had had "a little too much St. Patrick's Day."

In this particular case, the young girl, whom we ulti-mately learned was fifteen years old, had no identification with her. No name, no cards or wallet. Nothing. Her dun-garees and thin jacket contained only a single dime and a jar of Vaseline. Not even Sherlock Holmes could have done much with that.

Yet there was a peculiar and exaggerated intensity, an underlying hysteria that seemed to indicate more than a severe drug response. I would learn later that my percep-tion was accurate.

I turned from her to find a security guard assisting two young men who were dragging a friend through the main doors. Nurses ran out to help pull the casualty onto a stretcher. The boy's face was covered with blood and he was vomiting profusely. His two friends looking worried, helpless, and near tears, were standing awkwardly by. We sat them down in the waiting area and told them that the wait might be a long one. They sat there in silence, all their macho drained, looking for all the world like two very young children, frightened and forlorn.

At my first opportunity, I went into the waiting room to ask what had happened to their friend and to see whether they could give me a family phone number to call.

It was a familiar story. Lots to drink, plus uppers, plus more drink. An argument with a stranger, fists flying, and their friend got beaten up badly—then he just folded.

Mom and Dad's number?

It was only 3 P.M. The boy's parents wouldn't get home from work until about 7 P.M.; his friends didn't know how to reach them until then.

Anyone else I might contact? Aunt, grandparent, anyone?

They didn't know anyone else I might call.

Timorously, they asked whether they could see their friend. Could they stay with him for a while?

Yes. As soon as the doctor finished his examination. But I cautioned that they would only be able to visit one at a time. Our small and congested setting did not allow for easy traffic and, in any case, we were always aware of every patient's need for privacy. Today, we were not only contending with our usual flow of patients but, as they could see for themselves, an extraordinary rush of youthful casualties.

By 4 P.M. that afternoon, the E.R. was a madhouse. In they came, more and more young people, by ambulance, by taxi, reeling through the front doors, one even being carried fireman's chair–style, sitting upon the crossed hands of friends.

One of the most difficult cases for me on this particular March 17 was a strapping young man who, like the infants in the early melodramas had been abandoned on the doorstep—or rather, dumped unceremoniously onto the waiting-room floor and left there by the boy who had brought him in. He, the Good Samaritan, was seemingly too frightened to face whatever repercussions he thought might ensue.

Here again, the young man carried no identification and was too far gone to give a coherent description of what he had taken. He was raving, babbling on angrily about what sounded like world issues, political in nature and apparently racist, although his references were so totally garbled that it was impossible to make any sense out of them. What one could make sense of was the extreme anger and frustration spewing out of a fogged-up psyche that was now manifesting itself uninhibitedly in the tone and intensity of his voice.

Hours later, after checking with him every twenty minutes or so, I was able to elicit a name—surname I supposed—and the area in which he lived. The name was rather unusual, hardly pronounceable and fearfully long, with such a long vowel–consonant ending that it might have been spelled in a dozen ways. I tried to get the correct spelling from him, but the young man either would not or could not cooperate. I had to do this on my own.

I spent nearly an hour on the phone with a telephone supervisor, experimenting with various combinations, trying to run down a list of possibles. The telephone supervisor made her contribution, as well. We were finally left with thirteen numbers. Not wishing to frighten anyone and knowing that the chances of reaching a wrong party were good, I started down the list. I'd call, identify myself, and ask "Do you know a young man by the name of Tad Wells?" When the person said "No," I apologized and said that we were trying to locate the relatives of a young man with too much St. Paddy's Day. He himself was not able at present to give us information.

Most people were surprisingly quite kind and concerned. They wished me luck in my search and sent good wishes to our sick young man.

When this ill young man finally did come around, many hours later—life's little surprises—I learned his family did not even have a phone. He gave me the name and number of a neighbor, whom I called and who then got in touch with his parents. When the father called me shortly thereafter to find out what had happened, I told him in what condition his boy had arrived in our E.R., what condition his son was in at present, and approximately when the doctor felt he would be able to leave the E.R. and go home. His father said he would come to collect him. Just before hanging up the phone, he added, "I'm ashamed of him. I guess I should have made him go to school."

When the father arrived and entered the room where his son was now resting relatively comfortably, he looked down on the boy a moment, and then said, "I'm ashamed of you."

The son turned his swollen face up toward his father—and spat!

Some hours later, after eliciting information from friends, comforting youngsters in various states of disarray, discomfort, and disgust, I was able to find out from the young girl who had had her stomach pumped what her name was and where to reach her family. This, however, was no simple matter. It took a long period of coaxing and wheedling and advice-giving for me to get this information from her, long after she was in shape to give it.

She said her mom would be too upset and that it was too far for her mom to come to get her. She begged us to let her go, saying she could make it home on her own. A long period of quiet time spent with this fifteen-year-old scared girl finally convinced her that it was in her own best interest to have her family take care of her.

She gave me the information I needed.

Some time after contacting her mother, the woman arrived at the E.R. "Well," the mother said, "I guess I really should have tried to get her into a program. She's been really depressed and into herself this past year. Last month she took an overdose of pills—tried to kill herself." Mother paused and ruminated for a moment. "I guess I really should try to get her some help."

The parade of young patients in and out of the E.R.— kids scared, hours spent on the phone, the hysteria, the fear and crying both because of the experience they had undergone and what they were sure would face them when they got home continued well into the night.

Slowly, little by little, the E.R. emptied and quieted. The nurses and doctors were exhausted. At 11:15 P.M., I finally closed my office door and started for home.

"Maybe next St. Paddy's I'll call in sick," I heard one of the residents say. That'll be the day!

SEVEN DAYS A WEEK . . .

"Miss, oh miss, may I go inside and keep my boyfriend company?" the attractive young girl calls out to me plaintively. "Couldn't I, please?"

I am passing through the E.R. having just exchanged some information with the head nurse.

"Let me check for you," I reply.

The young girl's boyfriend has tripped over a pothole while they were out for a stroll on this warm summer afternoon. Although there seem to be only a few minor abrasions, he has fallen in an odd position, and there is one that could be truly damaging, and the doctors want to be sure that the injuries are no more extensive than meets the eye. They decide to take X rays.

The E.R. is especially busy this afternoon; a severe case of hemmorhaging, a gunshot wound, the delivery of a baby, which almost takes place just outside the doors of the hospital. It is a crazily busy time and I know there will be a lengthy waiting period for the nonemergent cases. It might be a while before the young man's X rays can be processed and read.

The young girl tells me she has already been sitting out in the waiting room feeling bored and missing her boyfriend and "well, it isn't like he's having a heart attack or anything. It's only his leg." She continues in a stream of chatter. "So—and anyhow . . ." She only gets to see him once a week because . . . you see . . . *she* lives in Brooklyn and *he* lives way up in the Bronx and her parents don't like him anyway and she is sure his mother hates her, so . . .

A check with the doctor confirms my feeling that there will be a wait until his X rays are read.

"Why not. Of course you can stay with him."

Whenever possible, we allow a friend or relative to sit with a waiting patient. Time passes slowly when you're under duress (which most patients are or feel they are); company can reduce the fear and tension and make the wait more endurable.

In the cubicle, the boyfriend is resting with one knee slightly propped up by a blanket to make his bruised leg more comfortable.

The boy's face suddenly lights up as the girl enters the room. She moves quickly to his bedside. I leave them alone. It is easy to see they are romantically involved.

The doctor reads the young man's X rays sometime later and goes to share the good news that they are negative and that there is nothing to worry about. He whisks aside the cubicle's curtain and there in the melee of clothes and sheets and blankets are boyfriend and girlfriend doing what they probably do every week when they meet—making love.

The pair is so absorbed in each other, the timing so critical, that they aren't aware of the doctor, and as he watches, astounded, he hears an enthusiastic and memorable cry: "Giddyap! Hi ho, Silver! We're off and riding, honey!"

■ ■ ■

It is about 11:30 P.M. A gentleman wearing a fancy felt cowboy hat, a city suit, and boots strides up to the window with a young man at his side. His companion is holding a towel up to his face.

"One of the camera crew took a bad spill. We think he may have a broken jaw. Can someone take a look at him?"

"Certainly," replies the clerk.

Nurse Jean Adams is called to escort the young man into the E.R.

"I'll give you whatever information you need for registration," says the gentleman to the clerk.

"Thank you," the clerk replies and begins to ask the pertinent questions.

"Oh, oh my goodness," a woman waiting with her husband to be seen for an infected finger whispers breathlessly, "that's Robert Redford!"

Without an upward glance, the husband shrugs his shoulders and with obvious irritation, shushes her.

"Don't be silly. What would Robert Redford be doing here? He's in the movies."

Robert Redford gives us all the necessary information on his crew member. The man had fallen off a scaffold during work on a film being shot just blocks away from the hospital.

We suggest that Mr. Redford may be more comfortable while he waits for the young man to be worked up if he goes to a watering hole near the hospital, since people are beginning to recognize and "corner" him. He is grateful for our suggestion. He will keep calling in to see how things are going, as he is very concerned.

"Oh, lord!" Jean, who has just exchanged the paper with the phone numbers for calling, insists she will never wash her hands again. She has just touched Robert Redford's hand.

"You'll have to change professions," quips the doctor.

■ ■ ■

A male patient is brought in suffering a stroke. After being stabilized in the E.R., he is taken to a Special Care Unit, where he dies three days later. A week goes by and I then receive an explosive and irate call from the brother of the dead man. He is furious that so much time elapsed before the family was notified, and then, finally, it was by the police. He wants to know why he wasn't contacted the minute his brother was taken to the E.R. He rages against our incompetence.

I spend hours pursuing the thin clues of this case, and track down the story. We've been unjustly accused.

The patient had started dating a lady about a month earlier. For whatever personal reasons, he had told the lady friend that his name was John Smith. The lady knew him by that name only, though they had dated often and, she implied, intimately, during that month. The lady did not know where John Smith lived, as Mr. Smith had always called on her at her place.

Then, while visiting his lady friend, Mr. Smith had had the stroke. In a panic, she called for the ambulance that brought him into our E.R.

In his pants' pocket, there was a billfold containing a few hundred dollars, but his wallet was leather-naked—not a single scrap of paper, not a card, no information by which we could possibly identify him. However, the lady kept assuring us that his name was John Smith. Improbable as it seemed, we nevertheless started looking for a Smith family, and we asked the help of the police in checking out that name.

It was a week later that the police succeeded in tracing the man's real identity and was able to contact his family. Evidently, the police hadn't told them about their brother's using an alias; they had said merely said that he had died, and from what, and where.

When I give him the whole story, the brother apologizes repeatedly and adds, "I hope he died happy."

■   ■   ■

"A heart attack! A heart attack!"

The woman's scream startles the entire E.R., which

until then had been comparatively quiet. All the waiting patients turn to stare. Attention is drawn away from center stage, where a plump young woman has been nursing an infant from overflowing breasts.

"I'm having a heart attack. Help me!"

This woman, dressed in a tattered housedress, shoes with broken straps, and stockings that are fallen down and rolled around her ankles leans into the clerk's window, screaming her need.

Apparently, she smells like an overripe Camembert cheese, for the clerk sniffs, backs away, then backs away still farther when he notices little critters jumping from her hair onto her filthy neck.

A nurse is called immediately and Bea Olsen comes in. Suddenly the screaming stops. The woman's hands fall away from clutching at her heart.

"Oh, hi. I remember you," she says, a smile growing on her face. The grievous "heart attack" is now forgotten. "Ya know, Nursie, nobody will listen ta me. Nobody," she whispers confidentially.

"What's the matter? What seems to be troubling you today? How are you feeling?" Bea's tone is intimate but she keeps her distance from the ubiquitous lice. "I haven't seen you in a while."

"Yeah. I been in the Bellevue psych ward, but then they let me out and now I don't eat regular anymore." Then, abruptly, she says, "I got a pain in my pulse."

"Show me."

"Well, I really can't show ya, but it felt funny and I knew ya would help me. Ya know, livin' on the street ain't easy."

"I know." Bea is infinitely patient and concerned. "Well, we'll check you out and see what we can do. But first . . ."

First is a thorough delousing.

The woman is asked to undress and she agrees silently. Her clothes are taken away to be destroyed. She allows herself to be led to a shower stall where a nurse's aide dressed in a disposable waterproof outfit is ready to wash her down. The woman stands happily deluged under the powerful streams of water; she is soaped with a substance referred to by staff as the Genghis Khan of delousing formulas. It is guaranteed to wipe out platoons, nay, a whole army of the little critters.

The woman begins to croak lustily. "I'm singin' in the rain." The aide laughs and begins to accompany her in the song.

Finally, when our lady of the streets is shiny clean, she is led into one of the cubicles and checked over by a doctor. Her condition is almost excellent, a bit undernourished but otherwise "A-okay," she is told.

A psychiatric consultation follows. Then an effort is made by staff to link her up in some hostel where a good meal and a chance to sleep indoors will be provided—probably the Women's Shelter. Fortunately, there is a bed available there. An appointment is then set up for a follow-up psychiatric session at Bellevue, where the woman's primary therapist is.

This woman could be fifty or sixty or seventy. She isn't. She is only twenty-two years old.

6 THE PRESIDENT IS IN TOWN

During the time that President Carter was finishing out his term of office, I was already at work in the E.R. at Roosevelt. One fall morning, just as I had settled myself at my desk, I was paged to the hospital's administrative office.

I arrived to be greeted by two very tall men who looked as though they had been cloned from a single DNA chain. Big men, both of them. Football tackles. Both were tan-suited, brown-eyed, perfectly groomed, and vacuously handsome; both wore their hair cut very short. Their piercing eyes seemed to be scanning and reviewing me as I entered.

They immediately introduced themselves as United States Secret Service agents and stated reverentially that "they were assigned to the care and protection of the President of the United States." Curtly, they told me that they would like a few minutes alone with me in my private office.

Off I went, flanked by my escorts, and was shortly planted uncomfortably in my small room. I sat down and offered them chairs.

"No, thank you," they stated emphatically, as if a momentary relaxation was a cardinal sin. "No."

I had absolutely no idea why they were there, but the mystery and solution were presented in the first sentence uttered. "The President is coming to New York to go to the theater. A phone will be installed in your Emergency Room. It will be directly connected to the White House so that if anything untoward should happen . . ."

If anything untoward should happen. Meaning, if there were any incidents and the President should have to be brought into the hospital, there could be immediate dialogue between the staff that traveled with the President and the staff in Washington.

Arrangements had already been made for installation of the phone; it would be connected shortly. And then, bearing down authoritatively, they wanted to make something very clear.

"You are to inform all of your E.R. staff—doctors, nurses, clerks, everyone—that this phone is the Presidential phone. It is not to be touched. Even if it rings."

An imperative stated imperatively.

"Understand. *It is not to be touched.*"

Yes. I understood.

We walked over to the E.R. and spent several minutes determining together exactly where the phone should be placed when it arrived.

Once again, the gentlemen warned me, "Remember, even if it rings."

Certainly, I assured them, I would instruct staff that they were not to touch that phone. Absolutely not.

Turning abruptly with a snapped military thank you, they left.

A considerable time was spent informing the entire staff and lecturing them on the strict order concerning *that phone.* Those of us who were on hand when it was brought in by the phone company and installed were somehow expecting a telephone that was, in some magical way, different, an extraordinary instrument, even though we knew this thought was ridiculous.

A common black desk phone was installed.

For a time, everyone's eyes seemed drawn to *that phone.* The very implication of its presence was enough to rivet our attention. After all, John Kennedy had been assassinated. And Robert Kennedy. And Martin Luther King, Jr. There had been an abortive attempt made upon the life of Gerald Ford.

What if . . . but we did not have time to dwell on possibilities. The frenzied, overburdened, human-repair workday was already in motion.

I had been told that the President would be arriving in town about dinnertime. The day had been full, with meetings, more meetings, follow-up reports, and a return home for dinner.

At six-thirty, I received a frantic call from Amy, the nurse on duty. "I've got to talk to you right away. Something's happened."

"Do you want me to go to the E.R., or would you rather meet me in my office?" I asked, recognizing from her agitation that it was not, definitely not, a "Can it wait till tomorrow?" answer that she needed to hear.

"I'd better go to your office."

"What is it? What?"

"Just come. Please."

Off went my housecoat, not fifteen minutes worn, on went slacks and a shirt, and out I raced . . . wondering.

Amy and I reached my office door at almost the same moment. She was distraught, in such a state that I braced myself. Okay, I'm prepared, I told myself, getting ready for whatever it was she was about to lay on me.

"Look, I know your specific instructions were that no one was to touch that phone—the President's phone. Well, about half an hour ago, it rang. Okay. I stared at it and then went about my business. I told everyone, 'Don't pay any attention to it, just get on with your work.' Then I went in to assist a patient."

"So?"

"So . . . that damned phone didn't stop ringing. It seemed like forever, but I told myself that it only *seemed* like forever. You know . . . a ringing phone always raises everyone's anxiety level, and . . ."

I was beginning to get the drift. "It didn't stop, huh?"

"Damn it, it didn't. I went back to the nurses' station and one of the clerks said, 'For God's sake, it's driving me crazy.' 'You'll have to ignore it,' I told her, 'like the rest of us. We were told *not* to touch it.' And all the while, I'm thinking, Madness. Won't it ever stop?! I started to pick up one of the regular phones to call and ask you what to do, but just then we had a case come in by ambulance and I started running. Well . . . that ringing went on and on and on. Fifteen full minutes at least. None of us could stand it any longer. You know it was a tough day and that sound was driving us all to the edge. And it was getting to the patients, too. Frankly, it became unbearable."

She paused and drew a breath.

"I made a decision," she continued, "right or wrong. At this point I didn't give a hoot in hell what anyone had instructed me. That phone had to stop ringing. I lifted the receiver and in my most businesslike voice I announced myself."

She looked at me, her face a wash of guilt and rage and impotence.

"Oh, sweet Jesus," she said, "I sucked in my breath and waited. I guess I didn't really expect anything but a blank line at the other end. But . . ." she hesitated.

"But?"

"Well, this deep commanding voice yelled—screamed, 'We *told* you not to touch *the phone!* We specifically told you *not* to touch *the phone!*' I tried to explain that the noise was troubling the patients and was jarring to all of us, but he just said over again in that awful voice, 'We told you *not to touch that phone!*' "

Seeing Amy's near-tearful frustration, I suppose I

should have tried to control my reaction. Instead, help-lessly, I broke into laughter. Wild howls of laughter.

I was picturing that black inanimate object developing a life of its own and reaching out to haunt our staff; the recollection of those two starched straight-arrow Secret Service agents imposing their order earlier in the day; the idea of everyone in the E.R. trying to fill out charts and console patients and do examinations and prescribe medication while the phone rang shrilly on and on. Amy's decision, made with the best interests of all in mind, brought to my mind some cigar-chomping Army officer—a general, perhaps—berating the poor nurse that if she had been a patriotic American, she would not have answered an end-lessly ringing telephone in an endlessly busy Emergency Room. All these notions kept my laughter uproarious.

It was contagious.

Amy threw back her head and howled. Even after she had calmed down and left my office, I could hear her re-pressed giggles and then a chorus of raucous laughter re-sounding through the hallway.

That *phone!*

It is interesting to observe that the Presidential setup con-necting the White House to a host city's Emergency De-partments varies with the administration in office. Each President's visit to our city involves unique preparations.

The President travels with his personal doctor, and an ambulance is always assigned to him. Before his arrival, the Secret Service agents check out different areas of the hospi-tal that would be used, if necessary, for official meetings, for press and media, for family. They make arrangements for *the phone* even when the President is merely flying *over* the city. A sealed envelope, said to contain a detailed report on his medical history, is delivered and kept under lock and key in the E.R., to be opened only in a situation of dire necessity.

365 DAYS A YEAR . . .

A middle-aged motherly-looking woman is brought in, flanked by two burly policemen, one edging toward retirement, the other so young that, looking at him, I remember the wry saying that "You know you're getting old when the cops seem like little kids."

"She says she's having an asthma attack," the older policeman whispers, "but we think she's faking it. Listen," he continues, "you see, we were called in by the manager of the Crystal Hotel. A guest wanted to report the theft of three hundred dollars that had been lying on the dresser in his room."

"Oh?"

"Yeah. The guy goes down to the coffee shop for breakfast and when he returns, he finds this dame, this housekeeper, puttering around. The guy says he sensed she was surprised and nervous as hell. She was putting some finishing touches on making the bed. Anyway, the guy happens to glance at the dresser and sees the money is gone! No three one-hundred-dollar bills, just some twenties and change." The officer draws a breath. "He'd been gone about half an hour, he said. He left his dough because he intended to put the breakfast charge on his room bill. He said just before going down, he looked at the money, at the three one-hundred-dollar bills and thought, What the hell—he didn't want to carry it around if he wasn't going to need it. The hotel was large, modern, and expensive, so he figured it was safe. Anyway, he accused the woman right there on the spot and called down to the manager; by the time we arrived on the scene, the room was full of, you know, manager-type hotel people . . . lots of them. The guest was fit to be tied, but the dame, as soon as she saw us, commenced to have 'an attack.' " The last words are said with heavy irony.

"So, we have something of a problem." He looks directly at me. He wants something, but he doesn't say what.

There is a long pause. It becomes obvious that the officer expects his young partner to pick up the narrative.

"Well—well . . ." the younger policeman stammers, "like we said, we think she's faking it, or even if she is having a real attack of some kind, we think that . . ." He hesitates, turns a slow beet red, and shifts embarrassedly from foot to foot. "Anyway, we brought her here to be checked out medically and . . . and . . ."—again the stammer and the deepening blush"—we'd like the doc to do something for us.

"We think she hid the money . . . uh . . . on her person, if you know what I mean, and we'd like for you to check this out while you're giving her the exam for this attack she says she's having."

"Listen," the senior policeman boldly announces, "it wouldn't be the first time a woman used her private parts to hide contraband. Have the doctor take a look."

"I'm sorry," the doctor said, "we don't treat people in the E.R. for petty larceny, theft, or other such maladies. We treat people for their medical needs. I'll give her an appropriate exam now for her presenting symptoms." There is no medical need that the doctors can identify—no surprise to the police. She is carted off to the police precinct.

● ● ●

The man, middle-aged, extremely well-dressed, and distinguished-looking, his gray hair neatly trimmed, quite tall, one would suppose, were he not at the moment doubled over with pain, waddles into the E.R. He barely manages to make his way over to the registrar.

"Yes?" the clerk asks.

The man hesitates, then leans into the open glass frame and whispers a lengthy reply.

"I can't hear you." The clerk's voice booms across the room. One or two patients turn to stare.

The man's face flushes a deep red. "It's just that . . . just that . . ."

"You're gonna have to speak up."

"It's something to do with my"—the blush deepens further—"my penis."

"Can't urinate? Chancre?"

Once again, the man bends over to whisper. His face contorts with pain.

"I'd rather speak to the doctor, if you don't mind."

"Okay." The clerk shrugs. "Take a seat and we'll call you shortly."

The man waddles back to a chair and gingerly, carefully lowers himself into it.

Sometime later, the gentleman is taken into an examining room and removes his pants and undergarments, which he folds meticulously onto a chair. The doctor, Vinnie Lloyd, and Nurse Amy Hubbard, enter. The problem is now quite evident.

Doctor and nurse look at the offending organ, then quickly, almost involuntarily, they look at each other. Vinnie, who can be the funniest man on the staff, manages, obviously with great difficulty, to suppress a smile. Amy doesn't dare look at him. The poor guy is in agony. There, just below the head of the swollen, oozing, inflamed penis is a gold ring.

" 'Fourteen carat,' he said."

The gentleman shakes his head ruefully, tells his bizarre

story. The ring had been placed there by a passionate lover one week earlier. The lover, "a perfectly beautiful young man," had assured him that it would heighten the experience for both of them. "Wedded bliss, ring and all," he had said.

And it had. "Oh, how it had. Indeed, yes—but . . ."

The man flashes a look that pleads for understanding, a wistful, wry, awkward look. "But . . ." he continued.

But now?

The man has simply been unable to remove the ring. He has tried every kind of lubricant—butter, oil, Vaseline—nothing has helped. He has even soaked his penis in ice water for hours—"Damn near froze the thing; it looked like an icicle"—hoping that he could slide the ring off.

After a day or two of these ministrations, in which every variety of technique proved useless, he had decided, "Well, there it was and there it would stay—and the devil take the *hindmost.* Oops, sorry about that one," he added, his sense of humor rising to the surface. Perhaps, he had decided, it would heighten his pleasure and, "you know, bring an esoteric joy to—well—my next lover." The perfectly beautiful young man, never seen before this encounter, had never been seen since.

By the end of the week, however, the patient's penis began to smart, then pain, pain excruciatingly.

"Probably became infected from the metal underneath the gold plating," Vinnie ventures.

"Naturally," the man continues, "I can't go to my own private doctor. Just too embarrassing, you know. Besides, I'd throw him into cardiac arrest." So he had delayed coming for help until the agony became too much to bear—and here he was.

Vinnie takes another look, then sends Amy out for our trusty little ring-cutter, one of the many special items we keep in the E.R., although usually not for *this* purpose.

Now that the man is on the verge of being rid of his

incubus, a small smile plays around his mouth.

"Careful, Doc, with the family jewels!"

It takes only a minute to snip the ring off. It will take several weeks on antibiotics—and celibacy—to clear the infection.

Love in the big city.

■ ■ ■

Day after day, old people arrive in our E.R. They come in with broken bones. They come in with bedsores and other infections that are suppurating and seem to have been festering unattended for a long time. They are often emaciated, skeletally thin, spavined almost. Old people fall easily; their bones are brittle. Old people attempt to do things they are too frail to accomplish. Old people refuse to nourish themselves. Old people often resist help. On and on, a long list.

The care and protection of the elderly, who, along with our children, are the most vulnerable members of our society, is the concern of all of us. Being the weakest, they can be victimized most easily.

It bothers me . . . a lot.

■ ■ ■

I see him striding down the corridor.

Johnnie.

He is our "street person in residence." He literally lives on the sidewalks surrounding the hospital. Some days, he simple circles four blocks, going around and around from early morning until night, his hands folded over his chest, mumbling a constant stream of inaudible sentences.

In the winter, he wears many layers of torn shirts and sweaters, several pairs of socks under unlaced shoes, a woolen hat pulled over his ears (and when it is really freezing, his hat is pulled over his eyes, as well). He wears a glove on one hand, a mitten on the other.

In the summer, unlike so many of the other homeless men and women who float aimlessly around the city streets wearing their layers of clothes, no matter what the season or the weather, Johnnie sensibly adjusts his wardrobe for the climate. He will appear in an open cotton shirt, or a white T-shirt, or no shirt at all, torn khakis, or sometimes white undershorts with no trousers. Then, he is shod in summer sandals or, if they have been stolen (as they often are), he goes barefoot.

He is, of course, filthy.

Despite this, there is a charismatic quality about him. He is about thirty-five, rather good-looking, in fact—blue eyes, blondish-red hair, and a scruffy beard.

Generally, he moves at a very fast pace. If one was passing him for the first time, one would be certain that he was on his way to some kind of urgent appointment—with a doctor? A psychiatrist? A bookie? Perhaps the corner dope peddler? But no. His fast pace seems to be part of his pathology. He is going around in circles, at high speed.

Our E.R. is not his home away from home. It *is* his home. At least in his view, it is. He has set up this territorial imperative. It is his acre of space. His domain.

He scuttles in to use the bathroom and occasionally has been known to flood the room during his elaborate procedures with his "toilette."

Of course, he arrives to be attended and medicated when he is not feeling well. And many times he appears just to put a touch on one of our good-hearted nurses—money for a hot breakfast.

This morning he has come in to touch base with Amy, his favorite nurse. She greets him, takes a long look, and suddenly finds it difficult *not* to notice that his fly is open. The inch of underwear poking out rivets the eye's attention.

On closer inspection, it becomes apparent that although his pants are in fairly good condition, there is no zipper where a zipper ought to be. The Salvation Army does its best, but making major repairs on the clothing it offers is not a top priority.

Amy scrounges around for three big safety pins and while Johnnie stands immobile, his arms pointed outward as if to take flight (I have a swift image of the Crucifixion), she pins his fly shut, muttering softly, "Johnnie, if I get any of your lice this morning, I'll bop you."

Johnnie smiles, thanks her, and leaves in a good humor, carting away a closed fly, some spare change for a meal, and all the lice with which he arrived.

No nurse ever learned that part of emergency treatment in a classroom!

■ ■ ■

I have been called in to calm a patient who is waiting in one of the examining rooms for an urology consult. I confront a handsome rugged-looking man of about thirty, a macho, macho male, who is glaring at me, upset because he has already seen one doctor in the E.R. and he is demanding to know why the medic he's seen can't fix him up.

He claims he has a knot in one testical.

The doctor has advised him to see a specialist in the hospital, but our irascible patient does not want to spend time waiting for this specialist to come down to the E.R.

I patiently and painstakingly explain why it is to his advantage to wait. After all—a knot in his testicle. Some conditions, I reiterate, warrant a specialist's opinion and this is obviously one of those situations.

"I haven't had my lunch yet," he says belligerently. "Can you bring me some lunch?"

"No, sorry, I can't."

I think of all the reports and paperwork yet to be done. "Sorry, but it shouldn't be too much longer. Just try to be patient. It's really in your best interest to wait for the specialist."

He thinks a moment, then unconsciously runs a hand between his legs, caressing his crotch.

"Okay," he says, "I guess you're right."

"Well, got to go now," I say, "I hope you feel better. And you *are* doing the right thing."

As I turn to exit through the doorway, he calls, "Miss."

I turn.

"Hey . . . you know . . . you got nice legs."

Knotted testical indeed! He is, after all, a mucho macho male.

7 NEW YORK MARATHON

The marathon that courses each year over New York City is big news, widely publicized and completely televised. Early on the morning of the marathon, thousands of people gather at the starting point to enter the race. They must pass over bridges, run through marked-off streets through the five boroughs, most just in the hope they'll be able to finish; a few actually competing to win. Millions line the route to encourage the runners and to watch.

In the hospital, the E.R. doctors and nurses, all too familiar with what could happen in an exhausting event such as this, are also on alert. The general feeling here is wonder that so many people deliberately expose themselves to blistered feet, sprains, breaks—and those are the least dangerous potentials. Beyond that is the distinct possibility of a runner's working up a dangerously high temperature, sometimes reaching 107°F., and severe dehydration.

Why would people risk so much? Driven bunch, these runners. "Well, better get ready for one long day."

The race, on the second Sunday of October, starts at about 11 A.M. A few hours later—crisis time! By early afternoon, they will be passing through our department as though on a conveyor belt.

Prophetic?

No, experienced.

We were prepared. The ice machines were under pressure and buckets were ready. Massive amounts of aluminum wrap had been ordered and were at hand. Saline solutions were already stacked in neat pouches. Crutches, canes, and Ace bandages were in ample supply. Extra doctors, nurses, and clerks were on duty and a large supply of mops rested in a closet.

At 2:15 P.M., all hell broke loose.

The first of our ambulances roared into the courtyard, siren screeching. One EMT jumped out the back, the second EMT hopped out from behind the driver's seat and they rolled the gurney through the double doors and into the E.R. Their patient was a young man with an athletic body, now writhing and glistening with sweat. He was wearing shorts, sneakers, and socks, and he was babbling incoherently.

"Collapsed on the grass. He was moaning and holding his right thigh," the EMT told us as he maneuvered the stretcher. "He's been raving all the way in, but we can't understand a damned thing he's saying. Vital signs are lousy."

After lifting the young man onto a bed, the E.R. team went into action. Immediate coordinated action. Celia, one of the nurses, was rechecking his vital signs. Blood pressure seriously low. She hooked him up to an I.V. An aide came rushing in with buckets of ice to pour over the patient; water dripped from him to the floor; it was melting almost immediately from the extreme heat of his body.

A few seconds later, another ambulance careened up to the E.R. entrance. The ambulance doors swung open to disclose another gurney on which lay a figure. The number

264 sliced across his chest on a blue banner. He wore sweat-soaked shorts, a gold wedding band on his left hand, and no shoes. His eyelids fluttered slightly.

"No identification," the EMT said. "Picked him up along the marathon route. He seems really out of it. His temperature is hitting the moon."

In he went.

Another minute passed and two more ambulances drove up. Two more patients were easily recognized as runners by their clothes.

So within eight minutes, we had four men, all delirious, unable to answer any questions, all in a state of shock, each in a bed in a separate room, each an emergent situation needing *immediate* attention, the kind of immediate attention that might ultimately mean the difference between normal functioning and irreparable brain damage.

The terrifying exertion of running a marathon may have serious and sometimes fatal consequences. One of the most serious is dehydration, which can cause collapse. Body fluids containing electrolytes that are essential to nerve and muscle function and cell activity are dissipated by exertion and heat. Not only does the runner become exhausted, he or she "spikes a temperature," as the docs say, that can go as high as 106°F. and 107°F.—this is not unusual in these circumstances. A temperature of 108°F. is almost always lethal; even these lesser temperatures can cause temporary or permanent psychosis, damage kidneys and other organs, and can result in death.

Time is crucial in these cases. The minutes are desperate ones. The temperature must be brought down and the fluids replenished before irreversible brain damage takes place.

Under such circumstances, all of us—nurses, doctors, aides—became a frantically working ice brigade. We literally run to get ice from the machines into the buckets and take them into the rooms and onto the burning bodies, racing back and forth, almost like a fire brigade, to pour a continuous avalanche of ice over the patients. We slide, we slip, we slosh around dangerous pools of pink water on the floor, melted ice tinged with blood from the beginnings of hurriedly done I.V.'s.

Housekeepers followed us as we raced, mopping, mopping, mopping, wringing out the mops and repeating the process.

The scene was one of structured chaos, a multitude of tasks being performed by our teams of staff: checking vital signs constantly; taking temperature readings continually; putting information on patient charts; all working under the gun of the clock but each knowing precisely what his or her job was and each fulfilling those responsibilities with practiced expertise.

While this frenzied activity was taking place within the E.R., all was not quiet in the waiting room. Other casualties were coming in by twos and threes—some by taxi, some hobbling in on foot, some doubled over with stomach cramps, some with bleeding feet, some with broken bones.

The waiting room had an air of restlessness. Patients who had been there before the onslaught of marathoners were still waiting. They became aggressive in their demand to see the nurses. I carefully explained the reason for the long delay. It could be a matter of life or death. Most of those waiting seemed sympathetic and understanding. They settled back and were more willing to endure the long wait.

However, one little old lady, her voice pecking out each word, wasn't. "I always come here on Sundays when I have no one to talk to," she confided. "I dream up interesting symptoms to register so the doctors will be concerned about my case. But," she continued, rising laboriously from her chair, "if I'm going to have to sit around here with all these sick people just because those silly runners are inside . . . well . . . I think I'll just skip this time and come back again next Sunday."

In the four rooms, the nurses continued to monitor the vital signs of our critical patients. Luckily, the ice treatment was beginning to show results; temperatures began to fall, dropping a point or more at a time. The I.V.'s were beginning to replenish the loss of body fluids. Still, we knew it would be quite a while before we could consider these patients out of danger, with all of their faculties recovered.

At one point I stopped for breath and leaned against the corridor wall watching Jack Williamson attend to the most seriously depleted runner. After a moment, Jack walked wearily past the nurses' station heading for the next patient.

I was exhausted. Every bone in my body ached, my clothes were wet and uncomfortable, my shoes soaked. I almost wished *I* could lie down and be cared for. "How do you manage to keep this up?" I asked him.

"Every night when I get home," he told me, "my wife allows me a full half hour of primal screams."

A young man rushed past me headed for the men's room. He was green in the face and smelled like a combination of salty-sweat and limburger cheese. He was about twenty. He was followed by an older woman who positioned herself protectively outside the lavatory door as he slammed it shut. "My son," the woman said in explanation. "Every year he does it. Every year he vomits. And if I ask him, 'So are you going to run again?'—you know what his answer is? It's 'Well, you know how I am.' Same thing every year. And I say, 'You run in the sun. You collapse. They have to take you to the hospital. They have to pack you in ice. Then you vomit. You go home. You get up the next morning, put on those schmates, those rags, and you start running to get ready for the next marathon.' My son is a Ph.D. idiot, that's what he is."

The limp and weary young man slowly staggered out of the bathroom door. His mom followed after him and started to talk. "No." The young man shook his head, a direct signal for her to stop going at him. "Yeah, I know," he muttered, "but maybe next time . . ." The words trailed off sheepishly.

"You hear, 'maybe next time' he says." Mom raised her hands in the age-old gesture of resignation and despair.

They returned to his cubicle as a middle-aged man, dressed unbecomingly in a T-shirt that barely covered his swell of stomach, and with thin threads of wet hair plastered against his raw dome, was brought in and placed on the stretcher in the Code Room. His hands were clutching at his chest. A well-dressed woman accompanied him into the room.

"I tell you it's nothing. A little pain, that's all. Damn it! I was half a mile from the end and I couldn't run anymore. Damn! Started getting these lousy little pains. But I'm sure they're nothing. I think I'm just hungry."

"Yes, he is hungry." His wife bent close to me to confirm the fact. "He hasn't had a thing to eat all day."

"Well, let's just wait until the doctor has examined your husband," I suggested. Jean Adams was hooking up an I.V. and was preparing to monitor the man's heartbeat as Dr. Lloyd came in to examine the patient. Everyone is always on the alert when the symptom is chest pains.

"Damn, I'm hungry. *Hungry!*" the man reiterated petulantly. His wife, standing with me by the far wall of the room whispered to me, "Maybe that's all he needs. He gets gas if he's starved. Would it be okay for me to go out and get him a hamburger?"

A hamburger, thought I. The man might be having a heart attack. He might be a breath removed from death. And his wife wanted to bring him a hamburger to make it better. I understood in a human sense what the whole issue of denial was about, but I also knew that my role now was to keep psychological impediments from interfering with what the doctor and nurse needed to do toward making a diagnosis. I suggested that the two of us wait outside while the doctor made a thorough examination.

The woman demurred. No, she would not leave the room.

"She stays here with me." The man lifted his head from the mattress, and then bellowed, "I told you, I'm hungry."

Well, could she get him some orange juice at least? She looked at me imploringly.

"I hate orange juice" came the roar from her husband.

"Now really." His wife tried to placate him and turned to the doctor. "I'm worried about him. He's had some heart problems in the past, but not for a while now. Tell me, could the chest pains come from disappointment?" And without waiting for a reply, she again pressed her original point: "Perhaps a glass of milk?"

"Goddamn it, I hate milk, too. You know that. My belly's rumbling. I could go for a hot pastrami on rye. How about it, Doc?"

"Mr. Jones," Vinnie Lloyd replied with a patience I considered celestial, "I've examined you now and looked at some test results and there is some suspicion of damage. I suggest you be admitted to the hospital for observation. I've tried to get in touch with your family physician as you requested, but it's Sunday; the answering service says he's not available right now. Since you're from another state and since we are concerned about your condition, you should stay and get further medical evaluation."

"Doc, you're wrong. There's nothing wrong with me that some good food won't cure. I'm getting out of here."

Both Vinnie and I tried to reason with both the husband and the wife, telling them what a serious risk was involved in leaving. "Worry warts," muttered the man, "every last one of you." He signed the E.R. sheet, indicating that he chose to leave against medical advice, which relieved us of the responsibility of *his* decision. He signed with an exaggerated flourish, put on his shirt and shoes without a word, tightened the belt of his shorts, and walked out on the arm of his wife. Vinnie looked after them and sighed, incredu-

lous. "How long will that man last?" he asked quietly.
I wondered.

Heatstroke is a very dangerous syndrome. It can kill hundreds of people in urban areas during a heat wave (consider the cities in Texas in 1980). Long-distance runners and cyclists are particularly vulnerable.
The following advice is well heeded:

1. Runners should never attempt distances of ten miles or more if the temperature exceeds 82°F.

2. In dry hot weather (80°F. or more), long-distance running should take place before 9 A.M. or after 4 P.M.

3. Joggers should consume thirteen to seventeen ounces of fluids containing small amounts of sugar (glucose) and electrolites (sodium) at least ten to fifteen minutes before long-distance runs.

4. Runners should have fluid available for ingestion at two-mile intervals.

5. Runners should plan beforehand whom to contact in the event of a medical emergency. It can be of vital importance to the runner and to the hospital staff attending him/her. Runners used to arrive in the E.R. with no identification, nothing under their shorts and number but fevered flesh. Existing or previous medical conditions such as heart problems or allergic reactions are medically meaningful. Since the loss of electrolites can result in an incoherent state for hours, pertinent information was often unavailable. As a result of Roosevelt Emergency Department staff requests and suggestions, the runners now all carry identifying information, including name, address, phone number, next-of-kin and language spoken.

6. Runners should learn the early symptoms that signal heatstroke; these include throbbing pressure in the head, unsteadiness, nausea, dry skin, and hair on the chest and upper arms that literally stands on end (called piloerection).

ALWAYS OPEN . . .

"This one's a dilly," Jean Adams says. "I'm not even going to tell you what it's about on the phone. I want you to be surprised. We've just about thrown in the towel, so please come right over."

Over I march from the office to the E.R.

"What's up?" I ask, not entirely sure that I want to know. These surprises for which I am regularly summoned are generally crisis times and nerve-shattering in one way or another. I brace myself.

"There's a lady lying quietly on a stretcher in one of the rooms. She's got to be admitted—fell and broke a number of bones; doctor says she'll definitely need surgery."

"And what am *I* supposed to do?"

"Well, we just can't get her to let us put her valuables in the safe. She clutches her bag to her breast and won't let anyone touch it."

"Oh. That doesn't sound like such a problem."

"Oh, no? Listen—we explained to her that everything will be recorded in front of her and that she'll get a signed receipt for what we put away and she'll get it all back when she's ready to leave the hospital. We also explained that she can have someone come in and sign for her belongings and take them if she wishes. We told her all that."

"So?"

"So—uh, uh." The nurse shakes her head. "Nothing doing. She just keeps hugging that damn bag and repeating that everything she owns in the world is in there and no one—not one single soul—is going to touch it. When I asked her what 'everything in the world' was, she said, 'a few thousand dollars.' Well, I'm glad you're here. It's your baby now."

"Thanks," I mutter and make my way into the room of the lady in question.

A security guard joins me at her bedside. The rule is that *two* staff members must be present to check a patient's valuables.

"Good morning."

I say this quietly and calmly as I push back the curtain, my voice liquid with comfort and trustworthiness—I hope. "Good morning. I understand you're having something of a problem? You have some concern about your valuables? I've come to answer any questions you may have and see to it that your valuables are safeguarded while you're in surgery and during your period of recuperation."

No response. I move closer to the stretcher.

A tiny woman is lying there, curled in a fetal position, under a large sheet. Her face is turned away from me and all I can see is a mane of long and dried-out gray hair hanging loosely over the stretcher, and even at the distance I keep, pervading the air with an unwashed and astringently unpleasant smell.

"Listen," I say more strongly now, "you cannot take your purse with you when you go to into the operating room. And if you leave it anywhere, it could easily get misplaced or lost. You'll have to have your bag checked in *now*. I'll be happy to help you; however, it must be done."

"No! I don't want anyone to take my money."

"How much money do you have in your bag?"

The woman turns to me slowly and props herself up on one elbow, all the while keeping the bag close to her breast.

Then, after a minute's indecision, she painstakingly opens the snap, revealing a flood of bills lying there.

In direct answer to my last question, she commences to count the twenties, the tens, the singles, and the fifties. It is a slow, laborious process. Twice, she loses the count and begins all over again. Also I notice that she skips one sequence of numbers, so that I know we shall have to recount the money once again if we are to arrive at an accurate figure.

However, we are patient. After all, the woman is in pain, she is old, and she is frightened. So we stand by and watch as she painstakingly handles the bills. At one point about three quarters of the way through what seems like a final count, she suddenly stops, stuffs all the bills back into her pocketbook, snaps it shut, and plops down on her back. Pursing her lips in tight refusal, she says, "I don't want anyone to take my money!"

I leave the room and put in a call for the social worker. I am due at an important meeting; however, I recognize the need to help this woman feel more secure about what indeed does seem to be her entire life savings.

I return to her side, lean over, and put my hand on her shoulder.

"I know this must be a very frightening time for you—hurting yourself, needing an operation."

"I don't have anyone. No one! N-o o-n-e." She spells out the letters as though each is uprooted, torn from an inner field of pain. "Do you understand? No one."

Yes. I do understand.

"We're here to help you," I say as gently as I can. "We'll do our best to make you feel comfortable. Putting your money in the safe will be helpful, too. I assure you the hospital will take care of it so that when you're better and ready to leave, it'll all be there for you."

The woman's eyes are shut tight.

"Look," I continue, "someone is coming here in a few minutes. She and at least one other staff member will count out your money with you. Then we'll lock it up and give you a receipt, signed, indicating the exact amount you've given us to put away."

The woman's face contorts with the difficulty of making a decision. Then slowly she opens her eyes.

"Okay," she says finally and reluctantly. "Okay."

Passing the social worker in the hall the following day, I smile and lift thumb to forefinger in the "all's well" signal, continuing to move on my way.

"Hey, do you know how much that lady had in her pocketbook?"

"No," I reply as I whisk by.

"Eight thousand six hundred and five dollars and twenty-one cents." Her voice trails after me.

"And twenty-one cents?" I say, laughing.

"And twenty-one cents," she repeats. "After one hour and eleven count-throughs, do you think I'll ever forget it?"

• • •

It is a beautiful day. I feel like skipping the three blocks to the hospital, but I walk—a model of propriety.

I am no sooner at my desk than the intercom buzzes.

"The District Attorney's office is on the phone for you," my secretary tells me.

The District Attorney's office?

"Good morning," I chirp airily into the receiver.

"Hello." No answering chirp, no lightness—instead, a very authoritative masculine voice barks out, "I would like your help with a case that is coming to trial in two days."

I am not even permitted a moment to say "Yes?" before the bark continues, rattling on at a furious pace, no pauses, no breaths taken.

"Some four years ago, you had a bullet-wound case in your E.R. The guy with the wound got it as a result of a crime he perpetrated. He was in the middle of the crime when he got caught. Anyway, he's making all kinds of accusations and claims that can weaken the state's case, so I need to know a couple of things. Who were the doctor and nurse in attendance? Were there any other persons with gunshot wounds in the E.R. being treated at the same time this guy was there? Who can come down to testify when the trial comes up? I want the name of every employee on duty on that particular shift on that date."

Whoa—hold on, I think to myself.

"Listen, sir," I begin soberly, the edge of my chirp blunted, "I'll be happy to help you in every way I can, of course, but you'll have to slow down. First, I will not and can not give you any information over the phone. Medical Records will need your request in writing, on a letterhead representing your office. Second—"

"No time for that," he interrupts sharply.

No time?

"I can't believe, sir, that you haven't been working on preparing this case for months, if not years," I reply gruffly.

"That's true," he answers matter-of-factly.

"And yet you expect the hospital to gather this information for you now in less than two days? You've got to be kidding."

"Not kidding. Not at all."

"Well then, for starters, get your request here in writing by messenger and we'll do what we can to help the cause of justice. Four years ago is a very long time. The Medical Records Department will have to pull the E.R. sheets to find out who was involved in treating this man. And— checking back to see whether or not there were any other gunshot wounds in the E.R. at the same time—do you have any idea what that involves? It means pulling out all the E.R. sheets for that date and reading through every single one of them. Hundreds."

"I'm really sorry, miss. I meant to get in touch with you sooner." Not with a bang but with a whimper came the gentle apology. "I *am* sorry. Truly. But it's really important that you do this for us. A lot rests on this information."

"I'm hearing you," I respond. "Just get the proper papers to us pronto."

He did. And we did. The case was brought to trial. The accused, I am told, is now serving a long term in prison.

• • •

"What happened to this one?"

An old man has been brought into the E.R. by ambulance. He looks in basically good health, certainly a survivor, we learn from the I.D. he carries, of eighty-four peaceful years. But now he is injured. Well-dressed originally, he is now bloodied and disheveled. Walking through the outdoor Lincoln Center complex on a lovely spring day, a shortcut on his way to visit his daughter and grandchildren, he was hit over the head with a forty-pound piece of concrete picked up from the ground by a man who had been released just two days earlier from a psychiatric facility. The former mental patient walked aimlessly in circles after crushing the old man's head, repeating, "I told them not to let me out. I told them I needed more help. Now maybe they'll believe me and take me back."

He was carted away by the police; the old man was carted away in our ambulance and brought to us in bad shape, though conscious, with bleeding, severe lacerations, and a crushed skull, protesting all the way, "Let me go. I want to get to my daughter."

Now, he tries to get up off the stretcher to leave.

Looked at from his point of view, it's a conflict. Here is someone who has just been victimized. Yet we must victimize him further (so he feels). We know he needs to be restrained, in his own best interest. He is tied onto the stretcher to spare him further injury.

The old man is screaming. "Let me go . . . my daughter's waiting." He struggles to get free of his bonds, growing more agitated every minute that his freedom is denied him.

In the hallway, Drew Gold shakes his head. "He probably won't die," he says, "but it will be a miracle if he's ever really right again."

I leave the room to go to a phone to contact his daughter. She has been expecting her dad for a pleasant spring visit, a lunch and a long afternoon of talk about old times. It is unlikely that he will ever have that kind of lunch with her again.

Another New York City statistic.

■ ■ ■

"Normal," I think. "They look normal, but they can't be."

The rather ordinary-looking woman of about thirty is neatly dressed, invisible in a crowd, no doubt, but a force—a presence in her own home. I feel that. And the husband is a thin speck of a man. They cannot be normal.

I feel a wave of anger so strong that I am clenching my fists.

Who do they think they are kidding? Anyone with an I.Q. of more than ten can take one look and know that something horrible has been going on.

"She was playing and she fell down," the mother says with an air of mild concern. Poppa nods his agreement.

Bundled in his arms is a little girl of about four with bruises and abrasions all over her sweet, clean, pretty face. One thin arm holds Poppa around the neck.

I peer at the child. The thin little arms reveal circular sores in different stages of infection, some open and suppurating, some blistered, some scabbed.

The child is thoroughly passive and soundless. Not a whimper of protest, not a cry even when she is undressed by the nurse for examination by the pediatrician who has been called down to the E.R.

When the child's clean stiffly starched dress and white undershirt are finally removed, Georgia, the nurse, stifles a gasp, but I see her shudder. Georgia is a tough lady who has seen just about everything in her fifteen years in the E.R., but this is more than enough.

The child's body looks as though it has been batiqued in black and blue and accented with those ominous circles of pain.

The parents are standing in the doorway. "She's a clumsy child," the mother says, smiling apologetically, "really clumsy." Poppa nods his head in agreement.

This child will be admitted to the pediatric unit of the hospital. Any suspected case of child abuse is admitted and then reported to the Bureau of Child Welfare. This is a moment of respite for the child—the time during which the system tries to be certain that they have an actionable case of child abuse that warrants legal intervention.

The doctor tells me afterward that she has seen many such cases of injuries inflicted by sick parents. The circles are a common form of torture—lighted cigarettes pressed into the flesh of the "bad" child.

And more. And worse.

■ ■ ■

The evening is extraordinarily balmy and warm for early spring. There is a summer softness in the air. On this lovely night, an old soldier leaves the scene.

He dies, not in the explosive smoke and fury and chaos of battle, but quietly, swiftly, without too much pain, we hope, surrounded only by the sterile cleanliness of the hospital and the gentle and controlled weeping of his wife.

It is not unusual for a man in his eighties to die. It is a natural part of life's progression, and at his age, a natural time.

We talk to the media and give them the simple concrete facts as we know them. We talk to the Pentagon and tell them everything they want to know.

An old soldier, respected for his decades of contribution to our safety and our freedom, leaves the scene.

General Omar Bradley is dead.

8 RAPE IS A FOUR-LETTER WORD

I felt strongly and passionately that an advocacy program for victims of rape needed to be established in the hospital setting. It is now a reality of which I am proud to have been a part. I remember one incident in particular spurred me to work hard to institute this planned advocacy program.

New Year's Eve for many people is a night for desperate conviviality, for heavy drinking, for large crowds gathering in hotel ballrooms, for parties spilling out of houses and apartments. But my tradition has always been to spend an intimate evening with a few close friends.

So it was this New Year's Eve. I was having a lovely quiet time. There had been a carefully planned and shopped-for exquisite dinner, with fine wines that mellowed us all. Soft music was playing on the stereo and the conversation was animated, interesting, controversial, and sparkling. It always was when I was with these particular friends—friends with whom I shared a long and intimate history.

We now sat waiting for the whistles and booms and shouts from the street that would usher in the new decade.

Suddenly my pager, which lay propped on my desk, came to life. Beep! Beep! Beep!—the inevitable signal from the hospital. I lifted the phone and dialed. After one ring,

I heard the familiar voice of Carmen Sandoz, one of our nurses.

"Emergency Room."

"Almost happy New Year," I said. "Almost, but soon not to be, apparently."

"Sorry we had to page you, Saundra, but we've got a real crisis here."

"What's going on, Carmen?"

"The police just brought in a woman—you can hear her screaming, I think. Listen, Saundra, she was tied to a tree in Central Park."

"She was *what?*"

"I know. I couldn't believe it at first. But these two cops brought her in, and they're the ones who told me she was raped and tied up.

"We asked her if there was anyone to call," Carmen said. "She just kept up a violent kind of shaking her head and saying no! She just keeps wailing. She really needs someone to be with her. The doc has already seen her briefly, and now we're waiting for the gynecologist. And right now we've got a car accident, two heart attacks, and a lot of disoriented souls who couldn't even wait until midnight before getting zonked. They've been dragged in by friends and relatives, some so sick they're convinced they're going to die. Every room is full, and it isn't even New Year's yet. We need you here, Saundra, so take a last sip of whatever and please come."

So at 11:45 I was walking across the ambulance courtyard and through the swinging doors into the inner sanctum of the E.R. I thought I heard those terrible wails as I approached, but I had not. They were echoing in my heart, those piteous sounds I had listened to at a distance over my phone.

There was no way I could have remained at my apartment with my friends, enjoying fond remembrances of the past or toasts to the future. I had to be there.

I clipped on my I.D. Patients are entitled to know who

we are and the position for which we are held accountable.

I found Carmen in the Code Room monitoring an EKG. "Can you give me any more on the woman the police brought in from Central Park?" I asked her.

"We haven't been able to get any information from her. She was so hysterical, she couldn't really speak. The police tried to question her but I'm not sure what they found out. And I've been running like a lunatic all evening. Why don't you go talk to the cops? They're hanging out at the other end of the corridor."

I was on my way.

"Hi, fellas," I said. Both men had familiar faces.

"Hey, what's the boss doing here on New Year's Eve? Bosses don't work on New Year's Eve," the bigger one teased.

"Well, *you* do, so there's no reason I shouldn't. Listen," I said, serious now. "Tell me about the woman in the gynecological examining room."

The smaller policeman answered. "We were cruising when we got this radio call that there was someone tied to a tree right near the children's zoo. We figured it was a kid's prank, ya know, some kids who were bringing in the new year with a buzz on, but of course we went to check. Took a bit of hard looking, too. But then we heard some moans that led us to the lady. Jeez! She was tied up but good. And hell, she looked like she was plenty roughed up, too. A mess. When we cut the ropes she practically fell into our arms. She told us she had been tied to that tree for two days and two nights. She said she had been kidnapped by two guys a week before. They took her to some apartment and raped her on and off. They'd go out leaving her tied to the bed, then come back and rape her again. Then two days ago, they waited until it was dark, took her into the park, and . . . well. Sounds wild, doesn't it?"

"Thanks, guys. You'll be around for a while, won't you?"

"Yeah, we will. We have to wait until you can calm her

down enough so we can ask some more questions. We haven't been able yet to find out what her name is, where she lives, all that stuff. And goddamn it, we want a description of those two bastards."

All this while, the woman's moans filled the air. Now they threatened to crescendo. I walked toward the source of the sound, drew aside the curtain, and entered the room, where she was.

This was the only room in the E.R. that had a gynecological examining table—one equipped with stirrups. We had often used it for other than ob/gyn-related problems. I recalled briefly the man with the knotted testicles sitting on this very table.

There was a cabinet with some specula, towels, swabs, slides, rubber examining gloves, and sex crimes' evidence-collection kits.

On the table, a huddled figure lay curled on her side between two sheets. Her body was trembling violently as I watched. Her back was toward me.

A shock of thick black hair spilled down over the sheet, over the table, and straight out into the air, almost standing on end.

I was silent for a long time. She seemed to be asleep. She had stopped wailing and moaning. She, too, was silent.

I approached and placed my hand very gently on her sheet-covered shoulder. There was no reaction. I could not be sure whether she was not aware that I had touched her or whether she had indeed felt the soft brushing but had not one iota of strength left to acknowledge the fact that I was there. I touched her again, my fingers bearing down with a tiny bit more pressure.

Outside of the room, there was a sudden bustle of activity. A siren announced another arrival of an emergent nature to our doors, and the rapid scuffling of several pairs of feet racing down the corridor to meet it was unmistakable.

If the woman before me was within our reality, I thought, then surely she must have heard the commotion. Yet the figure on the table remained silent.

The patient—the victim—was a rather large woman whose body felt shockingly cold to my touch. An earthy pungent smell as of someone who has lived in the same clothes for too long a time surrounded her like an aura, like a malodorous shield. After all, the woman had reported being held captive for an entire week. Certainly, the police had found her tied to a tree—left in the December air—for two days and two nights. A long, long time. Terrible to contemplate.

I pulled the only chair in the room close to the table and sat beside her.

For more than half an hour, neither of us moved. Not a word was spoken. I did not break the silence, thinking that I must acknowledge that by keeping her back to me, she was telling me she did not wish to recognize my presence and that while what *I* wanted most was to help her if I could, *she* wanted and needed to be apart for just a while longer. Perhaps to her I was just another stranger appearing out of that harsh and horrible world that had injured her so. Perhaps she might feel I was intruding on her trauma.

Whatever support I could offer that would be meaningful would have to be out of *her* need and not out of what I presumed was her need. Her unresponsiveness was a cue to me. So, I would wait.

(The lesson stayed in my memory and later became one of the basic tenets of the Rape Victims Advocate Training Program: No advocate imposes advice, personal beliefs, or judgments. One must be guided in one's support to answer the *individual's* needs; one must listen and respond with the acute sensitivity of a performer dancing a pas de deux on a platter of eggs. Rule number one!)

Another half hour passed. There was not a rustle of the sheets. She seemed to have fallen asleep. Good, I thought.

I knew that her vital signs had been checked when she first arrived. There was no report of a concussion on the chart, nothing that would prohibit her sleeping until she could have a full examination by the doctor. Yes, she certainly needed sleep.

The examination to follow might be unpleasant, embarrassing, even painful, no matter how gently administered. Since an examination for semen, as well as for internal injuries, would be made (with her permission), no oils or emollients of any kind would be used—those could mask the findings. Only water. The privacy of her body would be invaded with instruments. She would need every bit of energy to tolerate what might be further pain, added trauma.

Movement. The white sheet stirred and the woman rolled onto her back. It was the first chance to see the face of the woman I had stroked, the woman with whom I had kept the hour-long silent vigil and about whose most intimate and terrifying experience I was one of the few people in the world to know.

Her face, now that I saw it, was a mass of blotches, her lips black with abrasions, her eyes shut tightly against the world, were surrounded by heavy folds of swollen flesh. It was difficult to guess how old she was.

She began to mumble—tiny sounds of words—incoherent and undiscernable. In my gentlest tone, I told her my name, who I was, and that I was there to be with her. I asked what she wanted to say, was trying to say, but there was no reply. I bent over her trying to read her lips.

There was still no clarity in her speech. It was a toneless tumble of words coming from deep in her throat. She was someone awakening in a foreign country after a soul-searing experience, and was slowly experimenting with her breath and tongue and lips, articulating sounds just to reassure herself that she was still there—that she was still alive.

Now that she was slowly becoming aware of her surroundings, I left the room briefly to check on how long it would be before the doctor could give her a complete exam.

"Long," I was told. "There was another car accident, a bad one, a drunken driver now fighting for his life. So Happy New Year," Carmen said ironically.

I returned to the woman and took my place on the chair.

"It was terrible." The sentence seemed to crawl out of the dark cave of memory. Slowly, she opened her eyes and looked at me.

"It must have been," I replied—and waited.

"Where am I? What's going to happen to me? Why am I here?"

Careful. Careful.

"You're in the Emergency Room at Roosevelt Hospital. The police brought you in. As soon as possible, the doctor will examine you. We'll do everything we can to make you comfortable, everything we can to help you. We'll explain everything in your examination as it happens. And I'll stay with you for as long as you want."

"Yes, please don't leave. Please." Her voice quavered.

"I won't."

"It was terrible. Those two men. They took me away. It was a long time ago. I don't understand. They tied me up. They raped me. They raped me. They raped me. They raped me."

It was unbearable to watch her face contort with pain.

"They raped me. They raped me. They did terrible things to me. Why did this happen to me? How can I go on living? I can't go on. No."

She looked at me, her body one overwhelming question. "Why did this happen to me? Why? Oh God, if only I hadn't . . ." Her voice trailed off and her eyes closed again. She began to mumble.

There is so much to tell. Too much. So many, many cases.

I think of the young woman who got off a bus at the Port Authority bus terminal and was dragged by two young men into the men's toilet and sodomized. There was the college student who was raped in her own bed by a classmate visiting in her dorm room; the thirty-year-old woman who hopped a cab to meet a friend only a few blocks away and was raped by the cabdriver; the ten-year-old girl cornered in the ladies' room at school by five boys, punched, breasts fondled, panties torn off in a feeble and impotent attempt at coitus. In the last case, the boys did not succeed in breaking through her hymen, but she may nevertheless have nightmares about it for the rest of her life. There was the seventy-six-year-old woman cornered in the hallway of her apartment building and forced at gunpoint to perform fellatio. Recently, a small newspaper story tucked away on a back page—just a few lines that should have been major headlines—described a two-year-old girl who had been found suspended from a park tree branch by her ankles. Upon examination, it was found that this baby had been raped.

That New Year's Eve, I finally left the hospital and walked slowly home through the dawn. My friends were waiting for me, but I needed to be alone.

After they had left, with hugs and kisses and wishes for the new year, I left the dishes on the table and the empty wineglasses unwashed. I just lay down on my bed, curled up on my side with the blankets drawn around my neck, and cried and cried and cried.

In the past, a rape victim was forced to live and relive the degrading, brutalizing experience without professional support. Terror had to be overcome (and many times was not) alone. Often there was undeserved guilt: "If only I hadn't worn that dress"; "If only I hadn't gone out with him"; "If only I had fought harder. . . ."

The never-ending specter that also had to be borne alone. For centuries, most men have blamed the woman for

her rape. Until a few years ago, the law itself was an absurd-
ity and an insult, requiring that there be a *witness* to prove
the rape! Witness indeed! Rapists are not generally public
people.

Since the crime of rape leaves the victim with a sense of
no longer having control over her life (a common sign-
post), we have begun to call rape victims "survivors." We
are becoming more sensitive, more aware.

In August of 1980, a Rape Victims Advocate Training
Program was instituted at St. Luke's Roosevelt Hospital.
This program combines supportive crisis intervention by
volunteers—who go through an intensive training period—
and professional services offered by the Hospital Center
staff.

Every night an advocate is assigned to stand by from
6 P.M. to 8 A.M. Should a rape victim be brought into the
E.R., the advocate is immediately telephoned to come in.
Since one of the qualifications for advocacy is that the
volunteers must live within a fifteen-minute radius of the
hospital, there is no long wait between the time the survivor
arrives and the time the advocate is on hand.

The responsibility of the advocate is to stay with the
patient, guard the patient's interests, explain what is taking
place regarding treatment and why, and listen. She remains
with the victim from the first, accompanying her through all
procedures and stays until the woman is ready to leave the
hospital. The advocate will refer the victim for follow-up
counseling services if that is desired. Her primary purpose
is to provide desperately needed emotional support.

At the outset, the survivor is also going to need help
through the necessary and difficult processes that will ultimately be safeguards for her.

The natural instinct for those victims not in shock or
severely injured is to try to get clean—to rid oneself of the
"filth" of the experience. However, it's the opposite that's
desirable. For future medical/legal involvement and fol-

low-up, it becomes most important that the victim (a) does not take a drink or rinse her mouth until the examination is completed, since fellatio may have been practiced and it is procedural to swab the mouth for a sperm sample; (b) not wash her body, including the genitalia, so that sperm samples may be obtained; (c) under certain circumstances, have her pubic hair combed in order to find foreign matter such as a thread of cloth or male pubic hair; (d) have scrapings taken from under her fingernails against the possibility of finding cells from human flesh; (e) keep her underpants, which will be used as evidence by the police if she wishes to prosecute (note: new panties of every size are stocked in the E.D. and given to the victims when theirs are turned over to the police); (f) have an internal examination to check for internal injuries; (g) have follow-up care for protection against venereal disease.

If the victim is injured during a rape, she may apply to the Crime Victims Assistance Bureau for various forms of aid, including financial aid; that is, if she needs a new lock on her door or if she is afraid to return home and needs a place to stay overnight, or if she wants bars put on the windows of her home, she may get that kind of assistance.

The advocate remains throughout the medical examination, if the patient wishes. She encourages the survivor to ask questions and receive answers. Along with the doctor, she explains the clinical and legal reasons for the examination. In situations where the victims may not be able to cope with the police questioning at that particular juncture, the advocate may act as a buffer. The advocate will work with the police to help them obtain information, but always with the woman's immediate need as the barometer. The advocate may speak with family or friends at the victim's request, and help the important others to better understand the survivor's reactions (and their own), and more, her needs.

All advocates are prescreened and then trained in an intensive weekend-long seminar. During this period, each prospective advocate comes to an awareness of her own feelings about rape and the hidden agendas we all carry with us regarding this issue. The advocate is also given practical and useful information about all of the procedures the victims undergo in the Emergency Room. She will act as a bulwark of strength and take her cues from the needs of each individual survivor. The advocates attend monthly meetings to share the practical and emotional insights they gain with each experience.

These rape victims' advocates are actresses and writers, students and businesswomen, and stockbrokers and retired persons. The program has worked. Other hospitals have asked us to help them set up similar programs. Those of us who have been deeply involved and committed have been asked to write papers and appear on radio and television programs. The police department offers us kudos now and then. We get an occasional corporate donation to help us pay for the kits that are used for evidence collecting and for the panties that we replace. In the early days of the program, we needed underwriting for the training sessions given twice a year to educate new volunteers, for the information and follow-up services that we offer to rape victims in the form of group and private counseling sessions by social workers, and for a coordinator to administer the program, keep the schedules, write the newsletters, and answer calls from the victims. Now, all of that is built into the program costs.

The victims are no longer left to wait alone in a sterile room while others are attended. No longer must they struggle with their fear and horror in isolation. No longer are they thrown back upon themselves to find a way out of their trauma.

And finally, there are growing numbers of torchbearers to lighten the dark of this nightmare. In time, perhaps all hospital Emergency Departments will introduce similar programs to save the life of a psyche.

ALWAYS READY . . .

The back doors of the ambulance flew open. The EMT jumped out from behind the driver's seat and ran back to help his partner, who had been riding inside, ease the gurney out. They sprung the legs of the gurney into the locked position and pushed it speedily through the automatic doors to the Emergency Department.

It was a boy on the gurney, a tall overgrown kid. He looked as though every bone in his body was broken. Nearly every bone was. He lay there crumpled, one hand folded back against his arm like the sealed flap of an envelope.

In the E.D., there was swift purposeful activity. As the ambulance pulled into the couryard the nurse, quick, bird-like Carmen Sandoz was in the Code Room checking for supplies: the I.V. fluids that would replenish body chemicals lost in the profuse bleeding; the EKG machine that would record the heartbeats, a fine tracing of rhythmic black lines to tell the medical team what it needed to know.

Quickly, the medics rolled the gurney into the Code Room. With one swift move, long practiced and used, a nurse at the foot, two in the middle, and one supporting the head, the EMTs and the nurses carefully manipulated the patient from the ambulance's gurney onto the Code Room stretcher. Meanwhile, the boy's jeans and plaid shirt were being sheared off and peeled away so that George Phillips and his staff could look, prod, inject, suction, x-ray, monitor, and dilate.

The nurse moved quickly and quietly, watching the boy, the EKG machine, the I.V. drip in the boy's groin; listening and acting on George's rapid-fire instructions.

The boy had been picked up from his schoolyard, where he was a live-in student. It was a school for emotionally disturbed boys, one of the finest in the area.

It was almost impossible to believe the number of fractures on the boy's body.

"The drip needs adjusting." This came from one of the nurses.

George shook his head. "What a mess! If the kid's neck is broken—it almost certainly is—and if his pelvic bone is shattered and the vital organs punctured—Jesus, what's keeping him alive? A young kid like that—I'll never get used to it."

The paramedics were standing to one side, watching intently. As all EMTs and paramedics, they wanted to hang around as long as they could to see how it was going to turn out. They wanted to find out whether their fast arrival on the scene, their appropriate decisions, and their care would contribute to an ultimate survival. Or whether . . . they'd have to know that, too.

"It's a damn good thing you put on the mast trousers right away," George told them. "They kept his body stabilized. Good decision."

Hands moved deftly to intubate the patient—to get a tube down his throat to establish the airway. "Keep breathing, kid. Keep breathing," George implored. The sweat was pouring down his back; his shirt clung to him. I wondered whether he'd be able to use the tickets he had for a Lincoln Center concert that evening. They were going to be working over the kid for hours. But I knew that was the furthest thought from this doctor's mind right now. His concentration was total.

"It's a lot like making love," he had said to me once about the work of an E.R. team trying to save a patient. "The shared focus, the intimacy, the heightened adrenaline. And the elation when it works. . . ."

Now he was pleading. "I don't want this kid to die. I want him to make it! Damn it, I *need* him to make it!"

A clerk appeared at the Code Room door and beckoned to me. "The principal of the boy's school is here." I knew the school by reputation. It was one of the finest special schools in New York City, communal living on the premises. Progressive teaching. Lots of therapy.

A tall slender man in a conservative gray three-piece suit was nervously pacing the waiting room. He started to speak as I went in. "One of our boys . . . the boy in your Emergency Room. The school just notified me. I was at home today—a vacation day. How is he? Can I see him?"

"Not right now. The doctors are working very hard to stabilize him. But it would help us to have some information—we don't even know his name. Why don't you come into my office?"

"Yes, of course. Thank you."

He followed me into the room. We each pulled a chair out from around my conference table and scraped them along the floor. When we sat down, our knees almost touched. It seemed important to make close contact.

"Did they tell you what happened? What did happen to the boy?"

"The most we can piece together is that he went out the window of the room he shares with two other boys. It's on the fifth floor. Neither of his roommates was there at the time. We don't know—there's a suspicion that he might have taken some LSD and jumped—was impelled to jump—or that . . ." He stopped and cleared his throat.

". . . Or that he was deliberately trying to commit suicide. He's been a troubled boy all his life. He's been in therapy for several years now and we were hopeful that our school might be a chance for him. But now . . ."

As much to calm him as to get the information, I took all the facts: birth date, family history, allergies. I told the principal he could wait in my office if he wished, or go to the cafeteria for some coffee. There was no way of knowing how long it would be until I had something to report.

The boy had been a ward of the court for many years, the principal said, but there was one relative who should be notified of the accident. He would go have some coffee and decide how and when to place that call; he hesitated, fearful of what he would have to say. I watched him move down the hall, his shoulders sagging.

I was reminded of a young girl who had been brought into the E.R. about a year before—clearly a suicide attempt, this one. An overdose of pills. A medical student doing his rotation through the E.R. was on duty. He worked over the young patient for more than an hour, pumping and washing out her stomach and talking her back into the world. He later told me that this had been a first for him. He had felt marvelous being part of a team that had saved a young girl's life. For days, he had talked about it to his friends. It was obviously a milestone for him at the start of his career in medicine. He would never forget it.

Then, ten days later, she was brought in again. Same young girl. Overdosed. This time, she must have been discovered long after the drug had been absorbed into her system; or perhaps she had made sure this second time.

The student was part of the E.R. team again. They couldn't revive her. They couldn't get her back. Neither science, nor power of will, nor the magic of words could do it. As an aide prepared the body for the morgue, the medical student sank down on the one chair in the room and sobbed.

As she was leaving, the nurse put her hand on his shoulder. "Her demons were just too much for her," she said.

When I got back to the Code Room, I found it empty except for a housekeeper and one of the aides. The housekeeper was mopping the floor. The aide was restocking the cabinet: I.V. fluids, EKG paper, towels, and tape—all neatly replenished and ready for the next patient. The stretcher and the boy were gone.

I was stunned. Where was everyone? Where was the patient?

The nurse brushed by me as I reentered the hallway. "The kid didn't . . ." I was afraid to say it.

"No, it's okay. They took him to the O.R. He's gonna make it. He's young and strong. The doc thinks he'll make it. I think he'll make it, too."

■ ■ ■

In my capacity as administrator of the Emergency Department, I am sent a copy of the National Missing Persons Report each month. It is a small magazine called *Search;* it is published as a central registry of all persons reported as missing. Possibly one such person has come to us. The names, descriptions, and photos are sent in by concerned searching parents, guardians, spouses, friends, and agents, for the purpose of identification *only*. *Search* now reaches more than just the United States. It goes to more than a thousand law-enforcement agencies throughout Europe, as well as to agencies in the States. It may also assist in locating Americans, Canadians, and Mexicans who are missing abroad.

Its circulation in America reaches more than twelve thousand law-enforcement groups—municipal, county, state, federal, sheriffs' agencies, personnel at major transportation terminals and other public and private facilities, and court and corrections personnel. Its medical outreach is also extensive, involving hospitals, emergency facilities, clinics, and medical-referral services. On the social services scene, its mailing list includes agencies, youth shelters, runaway homes, public and private counseling services, rehabilitation services, volunteer programs associated with the criminal-justice system, and mental-health organizations.

An overwhelming list, but there are an estimated 2 million runaways, snatched, or otherwise missing persons who crisscross the country each year.

Each page of *Search*, which is only eight to ten pages in all, publishes photographs where available, and an addendum of detailed, precise clues that might assist in identifying or finding the missing person.

Each page is fascinating, frightening, and emotionally stirring, suggesting as it does the shadowy image of so many lives disrupted.

Each photo is labeled with the subject's full name and a *Search* number. A typical (in this case fictional) listing of facts accompanying the photo might be:

Nickname: "Mudgy." Born: April 30, 1975. Hair: Brown. Eyes: Blue. Height: 4'9". Complexion: sallow and acned. Last seen: about 6 P.M., June 13, 1986, at church festival. Circumstances: family argument. Medical history: allergic to beestings; heart murmur. Identifying marks: ¼-inch scar over left eyebrow.

On the first page of this publication, there is a listing headed SEARCH DISCONTINUED, indicating the *Search* I.D. number, the name, and a disposition such as "located" or "found dead." All *Search* listings remain active unless shown on this list. Only those individuals who have been found or otherwise definitely accounted for in some way will be discontinued.

The last few pages of this small magazine contain gruesome photographs of persons discovered dead—by natural causes, suicides, drug overdoses, murder—with whatever data is available and guarantees of confidentiality for information leading to the identification of the bodies. This might read (again, a fictional example):

Location found: Lake Placid area. Description: young, white male, about 17 years, 5'9", 120 pounds, dark curly hair, green eyes. Identifying marks: left ear pierced, 2-inch scar along right side of chest. Details: sources indicate name was Dusty; known to be street hustler; body found February 30, 1981. Cause of death: drowning. Agency: State of New York.

I look at the photograph again. It is the face of a beautiful boy.

My God! Seventeen years old. A child. And already a past street hustler—a male prostitute. Was he a murder victim? Or did he just give up?

Over 2 million people missing or dead—a staggering statistic! And most of them children from the ages of eight to twenty.

■ ■ ■

> *Humpty Dumpty sat on a wall,*
> *Humpty Dumpty had a great fall;*
> *All the king's horses*
> *And all the king's men*
> *Couldn't put Humpty Dumpty together again.*

The child's nursery rhyme runs through my head with a terrible insistence. I know now that no amount of medical skill will put *her* together again—ever.

It is eight o'clock in the morning. Ironically, a rare and magnificent morning—soft breeze, warm sunshine flooding through the windows, an ill-chosen day for suicide, it seems.

Suicides should take place, if they must, on days as cloudy and grim and dispiriting as the psyches that lead to them.

The ambulance brings her, a young girl in her twenties,

shot with her boyfriend's licensed .36-caliber Colt through her temple, by her own hand.

The story is not unfamiliar. A sensitive woman in love, an argument with her boyfriend, who, to quote some who knew her, "was her whole life," the argument becoming more heated, more ego-cutting . . .

In the Code Room, there is tension. The only sound is the stertorous breathing of the doctors as they work feverishly in an attempt to save her, and the sound of the pumping machines and the soft swish of the nurses' shoes on the floor as they move about. Effort, energy, and all that science can offer is teamed together to succeed—but everyone in the Code Room is aware that there is no hope. Nothing will help.

Humpty Dumpty cannot be put together again. There is no way.

I walk slowly down the corridor to the room where the family is waiting. Parents, siblings, boyfriend, all already beginning to create some patterns of guilt that could haunt them throughout their lives. If only . . . the inescapable thought.

I go into the room. I ease and comfort them to the extent that I can, to make these moments somewhat more endurable.

They are huddled together in a corner, their arms interlocked, holding one another.

I am suddenly reminded of an article I once read about a group of chimpanzees who were raised from infancy by humans. Then they were flown back to Africa and taught with a human's help to cope in the environment so foreign to them. There was a poignant photo of four small chimps, one behind the other, each clasping the animal in front, seeking support and closeness against their terror in this new and hostile land.

That's the way these people appear, huddling together against the new and terrible thing facing them.

The father breaks away to question me. He forces down his fear and his grief and tells me that he knows our hospital well; his father had spent ten weeks here several years earlier and had finally died a difficult death. He tells me how caring he feels everyone was to the aged man, as if to reassure me that he understands we are doing whatever is humanly possible to save his daughter and that he preforgives us for whatever the outcome. But he hopes never to see us again.

I take his hand and tell him *I* hope he never has to see us again.

There is no further time to talk. The doctor enters the room and as gently as he can makes the announcement. The girl has died.

There is a long silence. The cluster breaks up. Each one of them is alone with despair.

A while later, sensitively, we ask whether they would allow their daughter's organs to be donated for transplants. They are decent, people. They understand. They agree.

We lead them to a side exit. The father is the owner of a fairly well-known restaurant. It's not unlikely that the press will be around. We get the family out without incident; we will have to deal with the press. We will. We always do.

■ ■ ■

She is a very old, small lady, frail and sparrowlike, thin of flesh, her body quite clearly putting her age in the middle nineties.

The medical staff works tirelessly to resuscitate her. To no avail.

Undoubtedly she has died of "natural causes," but in a situation of this kind, an autopsy is indicated. There remains only the social and legal procedures to be fulfilled.

I look at her.

Her late life, the day-to-day patterns of her limited world are shamelessly naked, too easy to understand, almost too painful to acknowledge, encapsulated as they are in the worn black leather pocketbook that the police have brought into the hospital with her.

It does not contain much, only a few blunted clues to the loneliness of her years. Her name and address are printed in a neat hand on a crumpled piece of paper (she lived alone in a single-room occupancy); there are a few dollar bills, a key, a neatly folded handkerchief that has the dusty graying look of having laid there forever, unused. There is some string rolled up into a ball, a tiny bottle of perfume with a drop or two still not dried up, and a small, faded, well-fingered green address book.

Her life.

I know what her name is and so I sit with the worn address book in front of me and search through it carefully to see whether I can find a duplicate last name, a family member whom I can call to notify of this old lady's death.

There are many entries but none with the same surname. There are some sets of names that are duplicates of each other, indicating family connections, but who is who? Are they acquaintances, friends, relatives? Who might be most appropriate to call? To complicate matters still further, all of the addresses and phone numbers seem to be from out of state. There is not a single New York entry.

Yes—just one.

I discover the name and number of a Senior Citizen's Club. I call there. "Oh, yes," says the receptionist who answers. "We knew her. She used to come in occasionally, but that was . . . oh, a long time ago. Haven't seen her in . . ." The voice trails off into nothingness.

"Did she ever mention any family? Anyone?"

"Noooo . . . wait"—the voice becomes active again—"she did have one gentleman friend here at the club. I have his name and phone number, just a minute. He might know something more."

I thank her and call the gentleman. He is at home. In a quavering voice, he insists he has never heard of the lady, does not recognize her name, and why am I bothering him? He slams the receiver down.

Did the receptionist at the club make a mistake? Or . . . is the gentleman senile—or frightened? No matter. I must locate someone.

Once again I peruse the pages of the worn address book and I make a gut-level choice.

The address is a street in Beverly Hills, California. Beverly Hills! A sharp difference between its palm trees and palatial homes and a bleak spiritless single room on a rough West Side street in upper Manhattan.

I dial the number. A woman answers. I ask her whether she knows the woman.

"Yes, she's my grandmother."

"I'm sorry to be calling you with bad news, but . . ." I say softly.

The granddaughter shrieks into the phone. I put the dead woman's attending physician on (this is always the custom), a doctor to answer all the immediate agonizing questions that arise.

There will be no autopsy in this case, this at the request of the family. They have a religious prohibition against this "violation" of the body. Since it is not a suspicious death, the coroner's office soon clears the request to omit one. Arrangements will have to be made to have the body flown out to the West Coast or for the family to come to New York.

As I place the worn address book back into the bag, I think of what aftershocks will follow the death of this old lady. How deeply will it affect the periphery of all those lives listed in the address book—lives she touched once, long, long ago?

9 AIDS

Once every twenty minutes, someone in America dies of AIDS.

In the early days, when the disease was first identified in New York and San Francisco, all the patients seemed to be male homosexuals, and the health-care community labeled it GRID, for Gay-Related Immune Deficiency. That acronym did not last long.

The earliest experience I had with this dreaded disease was when a young man about twenty-five, ashen-pale and trembling, walked up quietly to the registration desk, leaned forward toward the clerk, and asked to see a doctor.

"Please fill out this form," the clerk said matter-of-factly.

The man, barely able to control the pen in his hand, began to write.

During the long wait for the doctor, the man obsessively tapped his foot; once the clerk noticed him wringing his hands. Used as the staff was to nervous patients, the clerk found this one out of the ordinary.

Finally, the young man was sent into an examination room to see Dr. Phillips.

The doctor noted the swollen glands and the rash called thrush that had developed in the patient's mouth.

"Christ . . . another one of those new cases of AIDS," George Phillips muttered to himself.

The examination of the patient was barely concluded when the clerk came stomping into my office.

"That patient breathed in my face! I looked at the E.R. sheet after he was admitted. Jesus! I asked George if it was another one with that new disease everyone's dying of. He shrugged it off." The clerk's voice rose several decibels. "But I know what it is. I'm going to catch it and die! What are you going to do about it? What?"

"Calm down, come on now, calm down," I said gently. "Believe me, from what we now know about this disease, you can't get it by being breathed upon. That's for sure."

It struck me then that much of the hospital staff, aides, paramedics, clerks—even the nurses—might be equally misinformed, and to avoid an interhospital convulsion, something had better be done about it. And quickly. It was imperative we start a full educational program.

"Look," I said, "I've been planning to have the Infection Control nurse come to one of our patient-care meetings. I'm going to set it up immediately so we can all get more accurate information about this, and people can ask all the questions they have."

The clerk seemed mollified by my honest answer.

"All right," he said grudgingly after a moment. "But I tell you right here and now, if I get sick, I'm going to sue!"

Pandemic. A widespread epidemic. *Panic.* Widespread terror.

With the growing statistics of the spread of disease in those early years, the media—the newspapers, radio, and television—were feeding the fear that was being generated. No longer were male homosexuals the only victims; AIDS was claiming intravenous-drug users, heterosexual men and women, even newborn babies. Hospital beds were filling up.

The terrifying period of incubation for this disease was

at first presumed to be a few weeks, then months, then the growing realization occurred that it could be five years. And then seven. Or nine. This led to another form of panic.

Since there was no cure, and the prediction for an eventual cure seemed a millennium away, those already afflicted and doomed could find no hope or solace; and for those safe at the moment, there were only questions. Was kissing a person who was known to be ill contagious? Could the AIDS virus breed in saliva? Or in a handshake? Or even by touching an object that had been touched by one with the illness? Was it dangerous to share an apartment? Was there risk in eating in a restaurant; after all, what did one know about the people who handled the food? Did sweat carry the virus? What about exercising, using machines in a gym? Or swimming in a health-club pool? Or donating blood?

Because there was little definitive data on the disease in the early years, parents began to be afraid to send their children to school. It was only after the New York City Health Department in collaboration with the New York City schools ran a three-hour seminar over closed-circuit TV, closed all the schools for the afternoon and recommended that all school personnel and parents watch, that the situation was somewhat defused. Experts formed this panel, and although there was some disagreement and some questions did not have positive, persuasive answers, the length of the program and the complete nonjudgmental review of all the known concerns and information led to a quieting of the hysteria.

To help combat the ignorance about the disease and its transmission, the hospital, through the Division of Infectious Diseases, decided to publish a brochure in which the public could find clear and straightforward answers to some of the most common questions about AIDS. It was in both English and Spanish and this information was made available in the E.R.

How could one get AIDS? How is it spread? These were

the most basic question. The answers explained that hetero- or homosexual relations with a person carrying the AIDS virus was one route of infection. Another avenue of infection was known to be through the bloodstream by sharing needles or syringes with one who carried the virus. The brochure suggested that drug users try to seek help to overcome their abuse, or, failing that, to use clean needles; and it listed a number of hospitals that had methadone maintenance programs. It stressed the use of condoms during intercourse and it spoke of the special danger of anal intercourse and anal-oral contact. It listed the symptomatology: swollen glands in the neck, rapid weight loss, thrush in the mouth, night sweats, and unusual skin discoloration or blotches. It also explained that some or all of these manifestations might be due to causes other than AIDS, but it urged that anyone who had these symptoms be tested.

The brochure also gave information about a variety of organizations that could give counsel and practical help to those already suffering from the disease.

DOREEN

She stood at one corner of the E.R. waiting room with two beautiful preschool children tugging at her skirt. We all remarked on the tenderness and patience she displayed toward them. She couldn't have been more than a teenager. When she was called in to be examined, she asked to take the youngsters in with her. She told Dr. Kate about her severe weight loss in the past weeks and how she felt "punky" all the time. Her husband of five years had been on drugs, shooting heroin. He had contracted AIDS about eighteen months earlier. She said shyly that she knew they should have been more careful when they had sex, but her husband flew into a rage whenever she mentioned that they ought to use rubbers. He had died three months earlier, and now she was mighty sick and guessed she should have a blood test.

If it was positive, she said, suddenly bending down to hug the children, even though her relations with her parents had been "lousy" since she ran off to get married, they had told her they were prepared to take care of her and the kids, no matter what the circumstances. She said she knew she was going to owe them a lot, but—"Anyway, I'm their kid and they love me, just like I love my kids. And it makes thinking about this a lot easier."

GLENN

He marched in with five friends in tow. They sat and talked almost boisterously in the waiting room, and laughed about a prank they had successfully played on another friend the day before. They asked for a piece of paper, then tore it into small sizes and drew lots. They planned that the loser would have to cook a gourmet dinner for Thanksgiving the following month, "Nothing traditionally American," he said, loudly enough to be heard across the room. "No ordinary turkey. Mozzarella with white anchovies; radicchio; shrimp bisque; and a broiled three-pound lobster. Cheese cake with crushed raspberry sauce for dessert. That's what I want." The dinner, with its uncharacteristic menus, was apparently a tradition that the five of them had shared for many years.

No hint of morbidity among them.

When he was called into the examination room, his

friends all clustered around and wanted to go in with him. This was not feasible Bea explained to them. One friend could go along while the others waited. The youngest-looking one, still a girl, was nudged by the others to go ahead.

"I know what it is, Doc," he said later, "I've already been to my own physician. It's AIDS. Listen, I'm here because I know you do research. I know you take care of AIDS patients and that you're a nurturing lot at this hospital. I want you to take care of me here. I want to know I'll have somewhere to go when it gets rough."

His friend began to cry silently.

JACK

He knew he was terminal. Admitted through the E.R., he was now an in-patient, dying from the secondary conditions brought on by AIDS. He had a number of infections; there was internal gastrointestinal bleeding and he now weighed barely eighty pounds. His "other one" (they had lived together for two years) knew it also. They had been sweethearts since high school and their relationship had carried through proms and football games and parties. Now he was dying and she could no longer give him the special care that he needed. After much thought, they decided to affirm their love formally. They would marry right in the hospital room, and, fighting the reach of time, do it at once.

They didn't want publicity. This was a private and intimate thing they were doing. But in spite of hard work and tightly buttoned lips, there was a leak, and the bedside marriage became public knowledge.

At once, the media descended on the hospital. "Who will be attending? What are the exact details of his condition? What's the prognosis? Why is the gal willing to marry this AIDS patient? What's she like? Can we interview him? Her? Them together, holding hands? Why won't you let us into the hospital? Is he your prisoner or something? Are you afraid of infection?"

The public-relations officer had gone to the patient after the first media request for an interview. While one might surmise that anyone so ill would not want to be interviewed, it still remained the patient's decision to make, unless or until the doctor involved believed that such a meeting was contraindicated to the patient's medical care. Not surprisingly, the young man did not want any contact or involvement with the media. His sweetheart, holding tightly to his hand at the bedside, agreed.

The state of siege continued. Dozens of calls plagued the hospital, all in an effort to find out at what time the wedding would take place. Even the European media pressed their inquiries. The priest who was to officiate at the wedding was sought out and he was hounded as well.

The hospital remained firm in its resolve. There would be *no* interviews. *No* cameras. *No* information. *No* comment!

The ceremony was short, respectful, and very touching. The bridegroom lay propped up on pillows, wearing a white shirt and tie for the occasion. The bride wore a simple white summer dress and carried a small bouquet of violets that he had ordered for her. They spoke their vows with a quiet intensity and kissed once at the end of the ceremony.

Still, the harassment did not cease. The press attempted to waylay those few staff members who had been witnesses, and again the media had to be reminded that the marriage had been a purely private event and any information about the patient was strictly confidential. No news would be forthcoming now, nor would it ever be.

The patient died twenty-four hours later.

HOWARD

His lover came into the E.R. asking for Nurse Adams. He was quite a rugged man, fortyish or so, dapperly dressed, with an air of sophistication. "I just wanted to talk to you," he told Jean. "You were so kind to us when my buddy was admitted."

"My guy is a beautiful man," he said slowly, "and a brilliant pianist who had a whole, wonderful future ahead of him. Now"—he leaned in toward the nurse—"it's hard. It's too hard." He sighed deeply. "And he's so gutsy. He wouldn't even join a support group—you know, he said that seeing others so ill would be like looking into a mirror and seeing himself. And that, he didn't want. So. . . ." His voice trailed off.

Suddenly his body sagged and he seemed to grow ten years older. "Earlier, when I bent down to kiss him in his room upstairs, do you know what he whispered? 'Like the aborigines say, I hear the roll of the drums. Have you thought about making plans for my funeral?' " The nurse embraced this broken man.

Working in the emergency department, I've seen so many cases where friends and relatives of AIDS patients, well-meaning, have been reluctant or afraid to treat the sick person in a way that would have been greatly comforting. I've seen others, wanting to help, who worried about what was the right thing to do. Because of that, I reproduce here

.a list of suggestions from the Chelsea Psychotherapy Associates, which I find immensely helpful in guiding those close to an AIDS patient.

WHEN A FRIEND HAS AIDS*

While serious illness is a fact of everyday life, AIDS has posed new challenges for everyone involved: not only individuals with AIDS, but also their friends. People who are in the prime of their lives have become ill, and their prospects for a long life have been severely affected. Their situation is not an isolated one, but is shared by people close to them.

When someone you know becomes ill, especially with a serious illness like AIDS, you may feel helpless or inadequate. If this person has been a good friend you may say, "Just call if you need anything." Then out of fear or insecurity you may dread the call, if it comes. Here are some thoughts and suggestions that may help you to help someone who is very ill.

—Try not to avoid your friend. Be there—it instills hope. Be the friend, the loved one you've always been, especially now when it is most important.

—Touch your friend. A simple squeeze of the hand or a hug can let him or her know that you still care. (You needn't be afraid . . . you cannot contract AIDS by simply touching . . . and hugs are very reassuring.)

—Call and ask if it is okay to come for a visit. Let your friend make the decision. If he or she may not feel up to a visitor that day, you can always visit on another occasion. Now is a time when your friendship can help keep loneliness and fear at a distance.

---

*Reprinted with permission of the Chelsea Psychotherapy Associates.

—*Respond to your friend's emotions. Weep with your friend when he or she weeps. Laugh when your friend laughs. Don't be afraid to share these intimate experiences, it's healthy to do so. They enrich you both.*

—*Call and say you would like to bring a favorite dish. Ask what day and time would be best for you to come. Bring the food in disposable containers, so your friend won't have to worry about washing dishes. Spend time sharing a meal.*

—*Go for a walk or outing together, but ask about and know your friend's limitations.*

—*Offer to help answer any correspondence which may be giving some difficulty or which your friend is avoiding.*

—*Call your friend and find out if anything is needed from the store. Ask for a shopping list and make a "special delivery" to your friend's home.*

—*Celebrate holidays and life with your friend by offering to decorate the home or hospital room. Bring flowers or other special treasures. Include your friend in your holiday festivities. A holiday doesn't have to be marked on a calendar; you can make every day a holiday.*

—*Check in with your friend's spouse, lover, care-partner, roommate or family member. Though your friend is the one who is sick, they may also be suffering. They may also need a break from the illness from time to time. Offer to stay with the person with AIDS in order to give the loved ones some free time. Invite them out. Offer to accompany them places. Remember, they may need someone to talk with as well.*

—*Your friend may be a parent. Ask about and offer to help care for any children. Offer to bring them to visit.*

—*Be creative. Bring books, periodicals, taped music, a poster for the wall, home baked cookies or delicacies to share. All of these become especially important now, and can bring warmth and joy.*

—*Bring along another old friend who perhaps hasn't yet been to visit.*

—*Don't be reluctant to ask about the illness, but be sensitive to whether your friend wants to discuss it. You can find out by asking, "Would you like to talk about how you're feeling?" However, don't pressure.*

—*Like everyone else, a person with AIDS can have both good and bad days. On good days treat your friend as you would any other friend. On the bad days, however, treat your friend with extra care and compassion.*

—*You don't always have to talk. It's okay to sit together silently reading, listening to music, watching television, holding hands. Much can be expressed without words.*

—*Can you take your friend somewhere? Transportation may be needed to a treatment, to the store or bank, to a physician, or perhaps to a movie or community event. How about just a ride to the beach or the park?*

—*Tell your friend how good he or she looks, but only if it is realistic. If your friend's appearance has changed, don't ignore it. Be gentle; yet remember . . . never lie.*

—*Encourage your friend to make decisions. Illness can cause a loss of control over many aspects of life. Don't deny your friend a chance to make decisions, no matter how simple or silly they may seem to you.*

—*Tell your friend what you'd like to do to help. If your friend agrees to your request, do it. Keep any promises you make.*

—*Be prepared for your friend to get angry with you for "no obvious reason," although you've been there and done everything you could. Permit this, and don't take it personally. Remember, anger and frustration are often taken out on the people most loved because it's safe and will be understood.*

—*Gossip can be healthy. Keep your friend up to date on mutual friends and other common interests. Your friend may be tired of talking about symptoms, doctors and treatments. Take your cues from your friend.*

—What's in the news? Discuss current events. Help keep your friend from feeling that the world is passing by.

—Offer to do household chores, perhaps taking out the laundry, washing dishes, watering plants, feeding and walking pets. This may be appreciated more than you realize. However, don't do what your friend wants to and can still do for him or herself. Ask before doing anything.

—Send a card that says simply, "I care!"

—If you and your friend are religious, ask if you could pray together. Don't be hesitant to share your faith. Spirituality can be very important at this time.

—Don't lecture or direct your anger at your friend if he or she seems to be handling the illness in a way that you think is inappropriate. Your friend may not be where you expect or need him or her to be. You may not understand what the feelings are and why certain choices are being made.

—Help your friend understand any feelings of blame regarding the illness. Remind your friend that lifestyles don't cause disease, germs do. This may be especially hard for both your friend and you. Help however you can.

—If you and your friend are going to engage in sex, be informed about the precautions which make sex safe for both of you. Heed them! Be imaginative . . . touch, stroke, massage. Sex need not always be genital to be fun.

—A loving family member can be a source of strength. Remember that by being a friend or lover you are also part of the family.

—Do not confuse acceptance of the illness with defeat. This acceptance may free your friend and provide a sense of his or her own power.

—Don't allow the person with AIDS or care-partner to become isolated. Let them know about the support groups and other concrete,

practical services offered without charge by a local hospital or AIDS service provider agency.

—Talk with your friend about the future: tomorrow, next week, next year. It's good to look toward the future without denying the reality of today. Hope is important at this time.

—Bring a positive attitude. It's catching.

—Finally, take care of yourself! Recognize your own emotions and honor them. Share your grief, anger, feelings of helplessness, or whatever is coming up for you, either individually with friends and loved ones or in a support group. Getting the support you need during this crisis will help you to be the real friend for your friend.

ALWAYS CARING . . .

They rushed him into the E.R. at 11:02 P.M. one Saturday night. He was a big man, about six feet six—huge. At that moment, he was bent over in agony, his face contorted with pain, although he did not utter a sound. I saw that both of his arms were held in a very peculiar position. He was in his police officer's uniform, as were the two men who escorted him in.

Shortly after his arrival, he was taken into X ray, then led into a cubicle to await the results.

As I walked in, my nostrils arched. A pungent odor permeated the room. I tried to disregard it and I asked whether there was anything I could do to make this patient more comfortable. Could I make a call to a relative?

"No, not until I know what the score is," he answered between gritted teeth.

Would he perhaps like a pillow to prop up his head a bit so he could lie down and be comfortable?

"No." Again the word chewed out of his pain. "I'd rather sit up—don't feel so helpless that way."

He tried to extend his arms in a gesture, a wan plea for understanding. He winced, then smiled a wan smile. "See."

I smiled back.

"But if you have time to listen, I'd like to tell you about

149

my day. Looks like I'll have a bit of a wait for the results of the X ray."

I look at the officer perched on the edge of the chair, waiting for my answer, obviously wanting me to remain.

Dealing with the numberless police casualties that turn up in the E.R., and aware of the dangerous nature of their work and knowing so many of them personally as good people, I have come to a profound appreciation of the burden ordinary police officers carry on their backs.

Of course I have time.

"Well," he begins, "I was loping through the theater district on my horse and. . . ."

Ah, that explains the odor. At once I am able to identify it.

"That's my beat, the theater district. And I saw this guy picking the pocketbook of a lady waiting for a bus. My horse and I picked up speed—it probably would have been faster for me to go on foot, but I wasn't about to dismount and let my pal fend for himself in that traffic. So I spurred him on and well, his hoof got caught between the cobblestones on the street and he threw me. There wasn't a way in hell it could have been avoided. He really took a bad stumble."

He paused and smiled a wry smile, "You know, there must be two, maybe three, cobblestoned streets left in the whole damned city of New York, and my horse gets his hoof caught on one of them. I felt myself flying through the air and I knew I was in trouble. But I didn't know how big till I landed. Pow! I went flying right into—would you believe it—the only pile of horseshit on the street. And I landed on my elbows—both of them. Did that hurt! Still does. I stink and I hurt."

Vinnie Lloyd, the doctor on duty, came in just then with the X rays. "So now," said the cop, "tell me about your day." "Not right now," I replied. "Let's see what the doctor has to say."

The mounted policeman had multiple fractures of both

arms; both arms had to be set and cast. "Mounted" and "cast," like the creation of a piece of sculpture—but it wasn't. It was the mean, nasty result of a hardworking policeman doing his duty—trying to save an old lady from being robbed. He would be spending many weeks at home, incapacitated and unable to take care of some of his most intimate personal needs without help. No work of art he!

Vinnie began the job of setting and casting. Later, when our New York mountie was ready to leave, he walked down the E.R. corridor and was greeted by his buddies, who immediately began razzing him. And little wonder. He stood tall, the Monster of the Cobblestone Lagoon; his arms, two huge white ramrods, protruded from his body, his horsey smell surrounding him—and reaching all of us.

As he left, he asked me to call his wife to tell her that he'd be a little late. Then, after considering and reconsidering, he said, "Tell her *why* and tell her to prep our washing machine. I've got to get this horseshit out of my clothes."

He grinned at his buddies. "Worse than skunk, huh?" As they left they continued to kid him and I overheard snatches of conversation: "You'll never get it out, fella!" and "Your beat will be a hundred percent pickpocket free— they'll smell you comin' for a mile!"

I called his wife and tried to soften the image of what she would be confronting when her husband arrived home.

"Oh, well, here we go again," she commented almost offhandedly. "This is the third set of broken bones in as many years with those horses. I'm going to insist that he take on a safer job in the department, like—like walking a beat."

■ ■ ■

A jogger out on a run has found him, his head gushing blood, lying unconscious on the grass. He is an old man. His dog, also old, was sitting by his side whimpering sadly, puzzled little cries, and occasionally he moved over to lick at the face of the old man. They were taking their regular evening walk in the park—man and dog, every morning, every evening, until violence struck.

At this time of night, the ambulance arrives almost immediately. The EMT's get the old man onto a gurney and into the ambulance. He is not in good condition. It is important that they get him into the E.D. as speedily as possible.

The dog hops into the back of the ambulance as if there is no question but that he will be going along with the old man.

The EMT's look at one another, make a compassionate decision, and shut the back doors.

At Roosevelt, the man is wheeled into the Code Room. Quickly, he is hooked up to an I.V. while his vital signs are being checked. The pooch has simply followed and now, as the charge nurse glances down, she sees the animal sitting immobile next to the stretcher on which his master lies moaning.

The nurse takes another long look and somehow, with a sudden acute realization, knows that it is part of her karma to take care of this dog.

But what does one do with a dog in the E.D.? Obviously, he has to be removed at once—a dog does not belong in this setting.

The old man has minimal identification. He lives in an SRO—a single-room occupancy. There are no phone numbers to call, no family we can notify. Just the dog.

There is no doubt that the old man will have to be hospitalized. The mugger has left him with broken bones, contusions, possibly even internal injuries not yet diagnosed.

So he is admitted, still unable to speak, still unable to give us a clue to anyone who might care for the animal.

It is eleven-thirty at night. The E.R. is bustling with more than twenty patients—and one sad, bewildered dog.

■ ■ ■

The nurse keeps the dog in her private office, feeds him, and on her break even manages to walk him around the hospital grounds. The dog is not overly happy to be cooped up in the small office for this hour. He lies listlessly at the foot of the door—waiting. There are other indications that he sorely misses his old friend, but he reacts to the kindness shown him. The wagging of his tail becomes a little more pronounced.

The dog for this time becomes a communal responsibility. He and his master bring home to all of us in the E.R. the specter of lonely old age.

Finally after much effort, we find an animal boarding home. A collection is taken. We all chip in to support the care of the animal for as long as it is necessary. One of the staff members takes the dog to his new temporary headquarters at the end of his shift.

This story has a happy ending. The old man finally recovers, after three weeks. He leaves the hospital. It is not difficult to guess what his first order of business will be.

■ ■ ■

The city is expecting a visit from the heir to the British throne, Charles, Prince of Wales. Handsome, charming, with the special aura that surrounds royalty, he is about to be married to the glamorous Lady Di. Charles's planned stay in New York stirs a great deal of excitement in this normally blasé city.

The visit stirs other emotions elsewhere. New York is home to a large number of partisans of the Northern Irelanders fighting for independence from England, and Prince Charles's appearances through the city are ready-made stages for demonstrations. Those demonstrations could turn violent.

We have alerted all of our Emergency Department staff scheduled for the four to midnight shift that on this particular night, Prince Charles—and Mrs. Reagan—will be within blocks of our ER, enjoying a performance by another group of visitors from England, the Royal Ballet. And that without a doubt, Irish Nationalist protesters will also be that close, demonstrating against the royal visitor and the government he represents.

I decide to remain in the hospital until the night is over, just in case. I can catch up on some paperwork, read some of the professional journals that are piled on my desk, and touch bases with my evening staff.

The E.R. is busy. There are two separate cases of rape brought in by the police, and two rape advocates have been summoned to the hospital to lend support to these women. One of the victims is eerily quiet; she does not utter a sound. She is in shock.

The other, in an adjoining room, is highly agitated. She alternately huddles on the stretcher, sobbing, or rises and rushes around, holding her head in her hands, screaming desperately, "Oh, God, what'll I do? What'll I do?"—loudly enough to be heard throughout the floor.

I hope the advocates arrive soon.

We are besieged with other patients as well—a bad skull fracture, a stabbing victim, a child unable to breathe. The workload is enormous.

I find myself shuttling between my office and the E.R., aware at every moment of the passage of time. I check my watch. It is 8 P.M. Well, one milestone has passed. The performance, I know, is just starting at Lincoln Center and thus far there have been no incidents. Good! This should mean relative peace and quiet at least until the show breaks.

I'm a cockeyed optimist.

At 8:35, my intercom buzzes. I stiffen, but there is no urgency in the clerk's voice as he says, "There are a couple of newspaper guys here to see you."

"Be right there." I wonder what they want.

However, as I enter the E.R. area, the E.D. doors fly

open. Supported between two EMT's is a tall burly man dressed in a suit and tie, soaked with blood down to his trouser cuffs from a nasty gash on his cheek.

The man is far from out—he is keeping up an unending stream of words as the medics help him to a seat.

"Bastards! I was just sitting there—it was frigging dark. I was in my seat when . . ."

I cannot hear the rest, as he is rushed into an examination room, Dr. Lawrence right behind him.

I hurry along to the registrar area to meet with the press.

"What can I do to help you gentlemen?"

"We heard that there were several people brought in here from Lincoln Center. Some kind of to-do with the Prince. Can you tell us about it?"

"Sorry," I reply, telling only half a truth, since from the few catchword phrases that whizzed by, I suspect that one of the to-do's has just trundled in. "I have no information for you at this moment."

"Well, can we check back with you in a while?"

"Certainly."

The reporters exit the front door, lean up against a post, and begin to light up cigarettes.

Damn, I think, they're going to hang around, damn well determined to land a juicy newsworthy item.

And from the bloodied babbling hulk that arrived, they just might pick it up.

I go back to the room, where the patient is sitting on a stretcher, occasionally glancing at himself in a mirror on a side wall. I learn that he has refused to give the E.R. staff any information—not a word about himself, not even his name. He is also refusing to allow the doctors to examine and treat him.

"I'm the administrator of the Emergency Department," I say quietly. "What happened?"

"I'll tell you. There I was, sitting in my seat, minding my

own business. I have a ticket for this concert, you know. I can prove it. See."

Into a pocket goes his hand and out comes a white half-stub, which immediately becomes smudged with blood.

"I see."

Back into his pocket goes the now-bloodied stub.

"Wouldn't you be more comfortable lying down?" I query.

"No! Bastards! Someone in my row hollered something. I don't know who. The performance was on and it was dark. The next thing I know, they're leaning over me. They gave it to me right in the face. I saw the blood gushing out. Straight from my face and down all over my suit. Shit, it's a two-hundred-dollar suit and just look at it—those bastards!"

I do look. No ad for Brooks Brothers, for sure.

"No pair of fists did this. They must have had something metal on their knuckles. They were in plainclothes, I'm gonna get them for this. You wait and see." He drew a breath. "Listen," he says after a moment, "where's a phone? I want to make a call."

"Certainly you can make a call. But, sir, you *do* need medical attention. We want to take care of you and it's important that you give us some basic information for our records."

"Look, lady—"

I forestall his answer. "Please understand. All our records are strictly confidential. It's for our use only. So, won't you please give us the data we need. Your name, address, and so forth?"

"Well now, miss, you're really a nice lady. Okay. I'll tell you what you want to know, but"—he faces me head-on— "I *don't* want to be cleaned up. I don't want the doctors to touch me until I have pictures taken. I want everybody to see what they've done."

I take down the information. I then lead the gentleman into an interview room, which happens to be empty at this time and where there's a phone he can use.

We enter and shut the door. He sits down at the desk and pulls out a rumpled, ragged piece of yellow lined paper. He dials. Waits. Then says, "Who . . . who is this?"

He looks at me, puzzled. "I got the laboratory."

"Oh, you got one of the departments in the hospital. You have to dial nine first and wait for the second dial tone."

He nods, waits, then dials again.

"Who is this?" He is shouting now. "Who? This is James. Those bastards, they bopped me right in the face. . . . No, I won't let them until you send someone to take pictures. . . . What do you mean, everyone is at the demonstration? You've got to send someone. I'm a mess. . . . I'm not going to let those bastards get away with this. Not on your life! What do you mean, where am I? I'm in the emergency room at—"

He looks to me for help.

"Roosevelt Hospital."

"Roosevelt Hospital," he repeats. "Yes."

He hangs up the phone and we both return to the treatment room. As he settles back onto the stretcher, my beeper goes off. The press has followed the spoor of the story and more of them are gathering in the waiting room. I will have to go out and see them shortly.

"Is your friend coming?" I ask. "I can understand why you feel it necessary to get pictures, but you must understand that your friend can take pictures *only* of you, and I will be obliged to monitor the process. We have to ensure everyone's confidentiality in the E.R."

"Yes, of course." He looks at me as though I have suddenly become visible—a presence. "You know, miss, you're very nice. I appreciate the fact that you realize I have to have those photographs before you fix me up."

"When will your friend arrive?" I am growing a little weary.

"Oh . . . as soon as possible."

Tricia Lawrence reenters just as I am going through the door, and once more the ritual of pleading begins.

"You know, sir, you've got a serious cut on your face. It needs stitches. We really should attend to that now."

"Not yet. No sirree!"

In the waiting room, as I have anticipated, there is a rapid-fire burst of questions from the reporters.

"We hear that . . . We want to know if . . . We understand that there was an incident at Lincoln Center and a number of people have been brought into your E.R."

"*One* people," I quip.

Again the barrage of questions.

"Can you give us a statement? Is he badly hurt? Where were his injuries sustained? What's his name? How old? Did it have to do with the shouting episode directed at Prince Charles?"

I heave a long labored sigh. "I am not in a position to tell you anything about what led to the man's coming here. You probably know more about that than I do." I look questioningly at one of the reporters.

"Not really," he answers.

"In any event," I continue, "the patient is being evaluated at the moment."

"How bad off is he?"

"We haven't finished the examination, but the doctor tells me he probably won't need to be admitted."

"Aw, come on, miss, give us his name." They are all wheedling.

"Sorry, gentlemen, I can't give you that information."

"Can we call you in a while? Come back later for details?"

"Of course. I'll be glad to share any appropriate data when I have it."

Feeling drained, I return to the patient.

It is hard to believe that well over an hour has passed since this man was delivered from the atmosphere of the ballet to the down-to-earth surroundings of the E.R. He is still soaked with blood that is already turning a deep hue of brown. And he is still adamant in his refusal to accept treatment.

"Look," I reason, "you said I understand your priorities. And I do. But our priority is to attend to your medical needs. And the doctor is waiting."

"I'll make a call again," he says determinedly, "but let me tell you, lady, if I have to sit this way in the middle of the street for the next six months, you can bet your life I will! I want everyone to see what happened." Back to the interview room with the phone. Out comes the crumpled piece of paper and he dials.

"Who is this? For God's sake, man, I told you before. I'm James. Didn't you hear me, bucko? *You know* who I am. Yes, they want to clean me up. Yes . . . we need those pictures. I'm holding everything up. Dammit! Who are you? Listen, I don't give a damn that they're all at the demonstration. I tell you they brass-knuckled me. I'm sitting here covered in my own blood. Yeah, they thought *I* was making the disturbance. I didn't do anything and I want those pictures!"

The phone is slammed back into its holder.

Back into the exam room. Back onto the stretcher. Off goes my beeper. More calls from the press. More calls from several radio stations. In comes the usual load of other patients—a victim of a car accident, a heart seizure. The waiting room is jumping. Another hour passes. It is after ten-thirty. I am not sure when the ballet will be over.

At eleven o'clock, I am beginning to tense.

"Can I call someone to come and be with you?"

"No, dear lady, I live in New Jersey. I came *by myself*. I just wanted to enjoy the ballet, and those bastards—"

This time *I* interrupt.

"Could you tell me who you are waiting for? I couldn't help but overhear. It was a New York City number you called."

"It was a newspaper office. I'm waiting for the photographer to show up."

"A photographer! I assumed it was a friend. I'm sorry, but I can't permit any news cameras in our E.R. You are free to talk to whomever you choose once we've treated you and you leave the hospital—but no press in here. Absolutely not!"

My antennae are vibrating. But I am not here to make judgments. It does not matter what circumstances bring a patient into the E.R. (with some exceptions; child abuse, for example, must be reported), the only pertinent issue is that every arriving patient receive the medical attention he or she needs.

It is time to lay down the law. I speak to the doctor. She and I will go in, personifying authority, and wind up the matter.

"We *must* get you cleaned up," says the doctor, looking as severe as she sounds. "Right now! We've got to take a good look at the laceration and suture it. If you wait too long, we won't be able to close the wound and you could develop a bad infection."

I back her up, "The doctor has told you what's in your best interest."

"But I must have everyone see that—"

"Yes"—I cut him off—"I understand. Now hear me. Dr. Lawrence has recorded your physical condition on your E.D. sheet. It can be requested through formal proper procedures. It will be kept in the hospital Medical Records files. When you leave, you can do what you wish, but at this moment, either sign the form and go or stay, get cleaned up, and have the doctor examine and treat you. The doctor and I strongly advise that you do the latter. But you must decide. Now!"

There follows a long pause. The gentleman glances at himself sideways in the mirror, then, he says, "You know . . . I think you ladies understand my feelings . . . why I want those photos, but . . ." Again a long pause ensues. "Okay, ladies. You're really very nice. I'll let you take care of me."

The delegation of two leave. The doctor instructs an aide to wash him down.

I glance at the clock. It is now a few minutes past eleven. I wonder whether the ballet crowd is emptying out of the Lincoln Center complex and I pray that the departure is a peaceful one.

It takes only ten minutes or so to suture the patient's wound. Out comes our patient, his tan suit and striped tie mottled with half-dried blood.

"Well," I say, "now I can see your handsome face." Indeed, he is an extremely attractive middle-aged man. "It's the first time I've really been able to see what you look like."

A beaming smile and a laceration of his nose confront me.

"How are you going to get home?" I ask.

"I told you, I live far away from here. I'll just call the newspaper number again, if I may, and take a taxi up there. I don't know anyone in the city."

So—once more into the breach. Once more we make our short trek to the interview office. Once more he dials.

"Hello, yes, they fixed me up. Where are you located? I have stitches in my face. My clothes are . . ." Then furiously, he says, "I can't go there. Okay, I'll take a taxi."

I decide to escort him to an exit and into a cab. I also decide it will be infinitely less harrowing to leave through the main doors of the hospital than run the press gauntlet at the Emergency Department exit.

He signs his departure sheet and is suddenly enormously cordial as the nurse gives him instructions on follow-up treatment with his own doctor.

"Ladies," he says, his voice cadenced as though making

a deep and courtly bow, "ladies, you've all been so good to me. And you are all so kind. I take my leave of you."

As we walk out into the warm spring air, I look at my watch. It is 11:40 P.M. I hope Prince Charles is now ensconced in his luxurious hotel suite, comfortable, cozy— and safe.

Next to me stands the ballet spectator, his clothes a mess, shaking my hand and reiterating his thanks, with an added invitation to visit him anytime I find myself in his neighborhood.

A taxi pulls up. I cannot help but overhear what he tells the driver as I am closing the door of the cab behind him.

"Do you know where Timothy's Bar is? Fifty-fifth and something . . ."

And the cab whisks off.

I look after it until it reaches the corner, then I turn wearily and walk home.

■ ■ ■

A pair of ultra four-inch heels, a sandstorm in San Reos, Brazil, a high-school prom in Dallas, Texas: All are by-products of New York City as an arts and entertainment center, all providing patients for St. Luke's Roosevelt Hospital's Emergency Department.

When *La Cage aux Folles,* the enchanting musical that dealt with the lifestyle of two homosexual lovers who owned a nightclub in Paris, was in rehearsal and on the boards on Broadway, problems not anticipated by the director arose.

Males from five feet seven to six feet tall made up the transvestite chorus of dancers in that show. They were dressed and bewigged exquisitely; and just as elaborate, ostentatious, and flamboyant as the costumes were the matching shoes, satin and bejeweled, with high spike heels.

The shift in body carriage from men's loafers to high heels provoked backaches that ran the gamut from a small degree of discomfort to a bent-over posture that needed medical attention. The Emergency Room provided refuge and relief. There they learned how to exercise before and after performances, when to apply ice and when to use heat to prevent or ease their pains.

What about that sandstorm?

On one of the decades-enduring daytime dramas, the story line had the leading characters stranded on an island off Brazil, and the script called for a ferocious sandstorm to threaten the male lead. Obviously, a five-show-a-week production isn't going to send cast and crew to Brazil to film one episode—or even to Jones Beach.

Instead, a set was built in the studio and, sand blowers primed and ready, the camera operators, grips, sound engineers, all the crew, put on face masks as protection against "sandstorm." The actors, of course, didn't have that option.

On cue, the sand blowers went into action, spreading a product called vermiculite to create the storm effect. Within minutes during the rehearsal, the floor of the vast studio was spread with a thick film of this dust. (Dust, it was learned later, that was potentially more dangerous than asbestos.)

The leading actor was supposed to be holed up in a cave, and he took the full force of the storm as it blasted into the cave. By midmorning, the man was almost totally laryngitic, almost unable to breathe, and definitely in need of medical help.

A protest against continuing the filming was raised at AFTRA, the television and radio artists' union, and the union came to us for information about the effects of breathing the vermiculite. Then, armed with answers, the union representative rushed to the studio and imposed an authority rarely used. She called for a total work stoppage. The set had to be thoroughly aired, the floor washed down, and all traces of the dust removed so that work could be resumed the following day. Then the camera angles were changed and rearranged so the scene could be shot without the hazards that previously existed.

In fact, the Emergency Room frequently serves as a "reference library" for the New York arts world. A director calls to ask what happens when someone has a concussion. "Do his eyes remain closed or do they roll upward in his head?" A mystery writer needs to know the symptoms in a case of slow poisoning. "Does the body change color?"

In still another situation, near-tragedy struck at the filming of a prom set in a "Texas high school." The shoot was in a huge room hung with colorful balloons and with one of those rotating balls of mirrored chips suspended from the ceiling. As the teen performers were gyrating, the huge ball suddenly dislodged and fell, knocking down a young actress.

The blow grazed her head and shoulders. She was unconscious for a few moments, and bleeding from the impact. We met her in the E.R.

■ ■ ■

I look at him, seated across the desk. Light, almost albino blond hair cut in the childish Buster Brown style; large round sea-blue eyes; a sweet mouth—a healthy, cherubic little Dutch boy look mounted on a six-foot-tall frame.

Now he sits, nervously running long fingernails up and down the palms of his hands, apprehensive, and yet with a trace of belligerence in his look.

Not without cause.

This discussion today can very well end in his suspension from his clerk's job. There have been too many complaints and too many inadequate and unreasonable excuses. He knows this. I know it.

So, there he sits, frightened, the chip on his shoulder diminishing with every minute that passes.

He seemed from the beginning like someone who really

cared about people. It was rumor, then fact, that he was extraordinarily "sensitive"—*temperamental* was the word most often used. There were growing reports of temper tantrums with the staff (which might have been forgivable) and sometimes with patients (which most certainly was not). His record indicated that he was out on sick leave almost more than he was at work.

Obviously a troubled young man—like the troubled youngster from the poem, who "when she was good / she was very, very good, / but when she was bad she was horrid."

I had called him in many times to speak with him, to encourage him to discuss his problems—because they affected his work—and to assure him that I would work with him to help improve his behavior and general efficiency patterns. I had warned him a number of times that he must attempt a change if he wanted to continue his employment in the E.R.

What was it? Surely he could tell me. What was bugging him? What was interfering with his doing an acceptable job?

There were always answers, subtle and evasive, and I had to confess to myself that he had revealed nothing and we had gotten nowhere.

During one talk when I felt that I was *almost* reaching him, I expressed my belief that the E.R. setting was often quite stressful—not everyone was psychologically suited to cope with it. Was that it? Would he perhaps be happier in a more tranquil, less explosive department in the hospital?

Not at all, he stated vehemently. On the contrary, he loved working in the E.R.. He loved the excitement of it, the spontaneity of it; he loved helping people. It gave meaning to his life, he said.

"Fine," I told him. "Then let's work together to create a new and more responsive image for you." But how could I help unless I understood what was bothering him? It would be impossible for me to counsel in a vacuum.

He leaned forward then, obviously wanting to speak, wanting to blurt out a reason—*the* reason for his irascible behavior, as though it would be a final relief. However, once again he drew back, unable to bring himself to reveal the truth.

The roots went deep I realized, deep and too tangled for him to articulate. The result of that and many other meetings would be just short periods of reform at best. Too short.

Now he sits opposite me, fully aware that this is the end of the line for him.

"You know why we're going to have to suspend you; your behavior is not acceptable. For heaven's sake, why don't you tell me what's going on with you; perhaps if I understand, we can salvage your job."

"It's hard. It's real hard." He is scowling. "It's real fuckin' hard to tell you—or anyone."

"Tell me what?"

"Well . . ." He rises and slowly crosses the room to a wall on which a small mirror is mounted. He looks at himself automatically, unaware that he is doing so. "Well, something major is happening in my life. It's been going on for some time now and that's the reason for—Jeez—for what you call my 'unreliable attitude.' And that's the reason that . . ."

He struggles to express himself, to finally broach the essential point. I sit and wait. It becomes a long moment. Then . . .

"I'm going to have a sex change!"

He turns and faces me.

"For the past year, I've been taking hormones. They really do strange things to me, but the doctor says that that's to be expected. I'm sorry about that, but all I keep thinking is that at the end of this long road will be what I've been wanting ever since I was a boy of five—to be a girl!"

10 THE DEATH OF JOHN LENNON

I awoke to the incessant beeping of the page unit that I kept within hearing distance all the time. I shot a glance at my watch. Eleven-oh-five P.M. Not so late at night, but I had been in very early that morning for the changing of the shifts the night before and had worked a thirteen-hour day and I was pooped. And to get a page now, when I had just fallen off to sleep! It had better be important! I roused myself and called the hospital switchboard. Connected to the E.R., I heard a tense voice at the other end. "There's been a shooting at Central Park West and Seventy-second Street, in front of the Dakota apartments. Saundra, it's John Lennon. The word's already out. Get here right away! The media is converging on us already. Crowds of people on the street outside, too. It seems like the whole city is here."

I slammed down the receiver. There was no time to think or feel. I threw on some clothes, grabbed my office keys, my I.D., the page unit, a five-dollar bill, and my home keys, and was out of the apartment in six minutes flat— some kind of record, I'd bet.

After several years of my tenancy, the doormen were well accustomed to finding me flying in and out of the apartment house at all kinds of odd hours as a result of my being on twenty-four-hour call, but my rush out of the building this night didn't give the sleepy doorman time to beat me to the door. I burst out under the canopy. A taxi was approaching and I hailed it, thinking it would be a faster trip by taxi than on foot, even though the hospital was only three blocks away.

On the short ride over, I decided it might make better sense to try the side entrance rather than go through the Emergency Room doors; the path might be clearer.

It was wishful thinking.

Hundreds of newspaper reporters and television and radio crews were already gathered at the scene, jostling one another, moving elaborate equipment about, and hurtling strategic questions at anyone who happened to pass by.

Chaos!

I forced my way, step by step, through this media maelstrom and immediately took a necessary measure with our security guards. They were to funnel all of these people into the main lobby area of the hospital. There, the reporters would be told that a statement would be made by our medical director at the appropriate time.

I then rushed into the E.R. I wanted to talk to the doctor who had attended the casualty. "The shooting victim" had been brought in by police car at 11:02 P.M., D.O.A. (dead on arrival), but, as in all such cases, a valiant attempt had been made to resuscitate him.

The doctors working over the patient had no idea of his identity until a while later, when the word seeped through. In such critical medical moments, the doctors don't waste time eliciting unnecessary details about a patient. Their efforts are urgently concentrated upon the saving of a life.

Thus, our doctors were not aware that the man for whom they were doing their "ordinary" job was an international celebrity. They all worked desperately in a final, heartbreaking effort—but it was to no avail.

. . .

Yoko Ono had, during this time, been ushered into an adjacent room with one of our nurses by her side. She was in an obvious state of shock, sitting upright, almost immobile in the chair, her fingers trembling, lacing and interlacing in an uncontrollable rhythm. At one point, she rose and, with a tiny flicker of energy, asked whether she could make a phone call. She dialed a number and simply said into the phone, "John has been shot. Please come to Roosevelt Hospital."

Again she took her seat and once more her fingers began to dance frenziedly.

George Phillips, the doctor who had been called, entered the room. Yoko tensed as he approached.

"I'm sorry," he said, "very sorry to have to tell you this. Your husband is dead. We were unable to resuscitate him."

She was silent for a long moment.

"No," Yoko said breathlessly. "No."

Two men arrived; they told the clerk that Yoko Ono had called and asked them to come to help her. They were on hand and gently supported her when she had to sign a receipt for the return of the cash Lennon had had in his pocket, as well as his watch and the gold chain he had worn around his neck. His clothes, we explained, were being held as evidence. As for Mr. Lennon—this was a homicide and there were certain procedures.

Yoko nodded her understanding. She signed the receipt, then shuddered, drew her coat around her shoulders, and allowed her two friends to escort her to a side door of the hospital, where, we hoped, she might be spared the flashing cameras and the merciless interrogation of the reporters.

Unfortunately, a huge cadre of photographers was lying in wait and the following day there was a large blowup of a picture of a sad and stressful Yoko Ono leaving through that doorway. "I want to go home to be with our son. *I* want to be the one to tell him," she said.

In the Code Room, the nurses had finished wrapping the body. It was then placed on a stretcher and wheeled into another room at the far end of the corridor. A bag containing John's clothes was carried into that room and placed on the floor beside the stretcher. In it were pants, a brown leather jacket with a fur collar, and boots—clothes that had been worn just a few hours earlier by a vibrant, exceptional human being. Two New York City policemen were assigned to guard the door of this room. They were instructed not to allow *anyone* in. I knew it would be quite a while before the chief medical examiner arrived, and I knew how ingenious the press could be and the various ruses they might use to attempt to get into the room, so I was being particularly cautious.

Now began the night-long onslaught by the media and the public. As I went toward the swinging doors by which ambulance patients are brought into the E.R., I saw that outside there was a sea of upright bodies flooded under the lights of television cameras; the ambulance courtyard was packed with people gathered around the camera and news crews, who were setting up angles and laying cables across the cement courtyard, most of them almost hidden by the hundreds and hundreds of people who kept pressing into the area.

Something had to be done. I went outside with one of our security guards to clear the courtyard. For despite the fact that it seemed as though every inhabitant of New York City was gathered there, I knew we would have our usual calls—accidents, mugging victims, perhaps a rape case—coming in.

I had to shout above the din to make myself heard by these newspeople to convince them to set up their cameras elsewhere.

"You can't block this ambulance yard," I told them. "I clearly understand the newsworthiness of this terrible happening. I understand your responsibility to the public, but I have my own responsibility, and that is to see that the ambulances have clear access to the E.R. We still need this space to be available. It's dangerous for the courtyard to be blocked with people. It's got to be cleared!"

Just as I was speaking, as though to prove my words, an ambulance with a heart-attack victim inside came careening around the corner and into the yard.

In the lobby area of the hospital, a medical statement was given to the press.

John Lennon was brought into the Emergency Room at 11:02 P.M. He had seven gunshot wounds in his body. Our attempts to revive him were unsuccessful. He was pronounced dead at 11:10 P.M.

The mob of newspeople went crazy, scattering, running off in all directions looking for available phones to call in their news.

The waiting room of the E.R. was bedlam.

Streams of people flooded in, identifying themselves as everyone from Yoko Ono's press agent, her secretary, even her hairdresser, to John Lennon's nearest and dearest relatives. I told my assistant and the security personnel to screen each and every one of these people personally. We found, with no surprise, that none of them were in any way connected with the family. They came, scavengers of sorrow, scavengers of tragedy. And the very number of them was incredible. We got rid of them quickly.

Calls to several police precincts in our area to ask for help in controlling the masses of people milling about and growing larger after the official announcement were at first unsuccessful. All the police not on regular patrol were, they

·told us, already confronted with the problem of mobs of fans gathering in front of the Dakota, where the Lennons lived and where John had been shot. They would try to send me help, but they were unable to promise it.

By a strange twist of fate, a young man had been brought into the E.R. earlier that evening—at about 10:45 P.M.—the victim of a motorcycle accident. He had been x-rayed and we found he had sustained several minor injuries. When it became known that Lennon had been shot and brought to our hospital, this fellow, who had been waiting for the results of his X rays in an adjoining room, jumped out of his wheelchair and ran to the pay phone in the waiting room. It turned out that he was a cub reporter on one of the daily papers and literally by accident had stumbled onto the scoop of a lifetime. He got his story in first and became the center of a great deal of attention; in his moment of greatness, he even tried to set up court in the waiting-room area—a brief reign to which I put an abrupt end. He was interviewed over and over again, however, outside of the building.

The chief medical examiner for the City of New York arrived at approximately 12:45 A.M. It was now December 9. I escorted him into the room where John Lennon lay and sent for one of the doctors who had worked over the body.

I felt the nurse's arm around my shoulder. "Are you okay?" she asked. "Sure," I replied. But the expression on my face and my wildly beating heart belied my answer. I looked away, biting my lower lip. I looked down at the floor. Something was wrong. Something was missing.

The bag! The bag of clothes was gone! It had been lying on the floor next to the stretcher. Where the hell was it?!

My anger was mounting. Damn! Imagine someone stealing those bloodstained vestments and peddling them off as macabre momentos. I had given explicit instructions that the room be constantly guarded. No one was to enter without my knowledge. *No one.* How could this have happened? Who was responsible? I opened my mouth to question the policeman, but he had already noticed my shock. "It was picked up by an officer," he told me. "He had to take it down to headquarters. Orders from the precinct."

"But why didn't you let me know? We need a receipt for those clothes," I heard myself growling at him. "You know we have to have a receipt."

"You're right. I'm sorry. I just didn't think. I apologize."

My fury subsided. "I'm sorry, too. I didn't mean to shout at you." It was, in fact, several days before I could actually locate the captain of the particular precinct where the clothes had been taken, and obtain from him the P.O. voucher number so that we could be assured (and Yoko also, in case, for whatever reason, she ever wanted to retrieve John's belongings) that the clothes *were* in police custody.

The captain explained that his officers had arrived in such a rush and had not waited to sign for the bag because they were searching for a bullet they knew was still missing. As I understood it, they had determined that there were five bullets fired. Seven wounds were manifest in the body, two of them obviously exit wounds, but they were able to find only four bullets at the scene of the crime.

I recalled then that one of the officers who brought Lennon in had asked me later whether we had recovered a bullet during the time we were trying to resuscitate John. We had not. Ultimately the missing bullet did turn up, lodged in the leather jacket Lennon had been wearing.

The medical examiner was now ready to leave. He asked me for the E.R. record we had established on Lennon. Medical records are never released from the hospital in a cavalier fashion; there is a careful procedure that must be followed. Given these unique circumstances, however, I told the medical examiner that I would give him a copy of our information but that he would have to sign a receipt for it. He did so willingly and said he admired me for my insistence on protocol.

At this point, the medical services that Roosevelt Hospital could render were concluded. All that remained was to place a call for a city morgue vehicle to come from Bellevue to pick up the body.

Outside, still, as far as the eye could see, camara people, reporters, and fans were backed up, block upon block, people spilling over from the courtyard into the neighboring streets. The ambulance yard was completely congested again, but, as though aware that one phase of the death of John Lennon had come to a close, the mood of the crowd underwent a subtle change. Voices quieted. Movement became muted. There was a restless hush, a solemn anticipatory air that lay like a fog over the area. It was now 1:30 A.M.

It was a fragile quiet, a fragile mood, and I knew that once the word got out that the morgue van was arriving, the mood might explode. There would be another wild scramble for pictures and information. I realized that we would have to plan a route that would keep Lennon's removal from our hospital as secret as possible.

I asked that the drivers of the Bellevue morgue van take their vehicle around to another part of the hospital, almost a half-block away from the E.R., where there was a loading dock for the delivery of hospital supplies. Fortunately, this was when the New York Police Department produced about twenty police officers who were ready to help us.

The doctor, the nurse, a security officer, and I rolled John Lennon's lifeless body—now completely wrapped and hidden under sheets (called a shroud)—through the corridors and down one flight in the freight elevator to a center hallway on the lower floor. I requested that the security officer, one policeman, and the nurse to remain with the body. Phase one of an overall plan was underway.

The doctor and I then led the phalanx of police to the loading-dock area. Here, there are two sets of rolling doors that rise from the floor to the enormously high ceiling. One of these doors opens into the hospital, the other opens onto the street. Between the two rolling doors there is a concrete platform large enough for several trucks and ambulances to park.

We walked onto the loading dock and rolled the door behind us down to the floor, cutting off possible entry into the hospital. Then the police stationed themselves in a line behind the front loading door that connected to the street. They stood positioned so that when the front rolling door was lifted, they could restrain the expected crush of people.

A mob had already gathered outside. We could hear them. Somehow they had smelled out what was happening and the volume of noise beyond the door was echoed and magnified within the cavern of the loading dock.

For a moment, I was worried for the safety of the police. "Don't worry," one of them quipped. "We've been in plenty of war zones. We can handle it."

Nervously, I gave the signal to open the front rolling door. As it slowly rose, I could see dozens of pairs of feet pressing forward and being nudged back by the line of police. It seemed almost impossible, but a space was being cleared and the morgue van began to back onto the platform. The police were struggling and I found myself waving my arms and shouting. "Keep back—*please* keep back! We don't want anyone to get hurt. Please!" Meanwhile, questions were being hurled at us by reporters.

Finally, the police were able to press the crowd back without incident, the space was cleared, and the van stood in place. The door was lowered. Now we had two sets of huge doors securely shut, enclosing a platform on which

stood one van, two van drivers, about twenty police officers, the doctor, and me. Phase two was accomplished.

It was now time to reopen the door that led into the
hospital. I rushed back into the inner hallway where the first
group of staff members was waiting with the body on its
stretcher. Quickly, we wheeled the stretcher onto the dock.
The van drivers took out their own gurney from the back
of the vehicle. The body was transferred onto it and they
rolled the stretcher up into the back of the van.

I could feel my back muscles begin to relax ever so
slightly. In a few moments, we would get the van out onto
the street. Once it was on its way, that part of my responsibility would be at an end. Just as I was expecting the drivers
to shut the van door, one of them whipped out an official-
looking sheet of paper from his pocket. "We have an order
here to pick up another body," he said matter-of-factly.

It couldn't be true! I couldn't believe it. After all of this?

However, it *was* true. The order on the paper claimed
the morgue at Bellevue was expecting two bodies—John
Lennon's and that of another person, which at that moment
lay in our small hospital morgue—an in-patient who had
died several hours earlier.

So we waited for the five minutes or so that it took for
the men to collect the other body and get back to the
loading dock. We stood silent in a circle around the van,
shifting our weight from one foot to the other, too exhausted to chatter, too benumbed by the night's horror.

Then, when this "other" was in place inside the van, we
once again closed the back door and watched the drivers
jump into the front seats and rev up the motor. The hospital staff moved back behind the rear rolling door and pulled
it down, leaving the police officers to open the front rolling
door and protect the van so that it could proceed on its way.
The last phase was complete.

I was more weary than at any time I could remember. The
doctor and I looked at each other. His face, etched with

strain, was sweat-covered and completely drained. I'm certain mine was, too. He had made his statement to the press, had spoken with care, dignity, and sensitivity, and I had orchestrated all the necessary behind-the-scenes activity. I encouraged him to go home and try to get some sleep. I knew that there would be countless interviews for him to attend the next day.

My work, however, was not ended. Calls were coming in from all over the world. The press and television reporters still hung around the ambulance courtyard. The curious were still invading the waiting room and, adding to this, other emergency patients were, of course, still arriving.

I told my assistant to keep abreast of the waiting-room entries to be certain that only authorized people and legitimate patients were admitted.

We had formulated a statement with which we responded to all calls. And they were legion! Their number and the callers' concern was an incredible mark of honor to Lennon. Calls came in to the hospital from New Zealand, from England, of course, from South America, Australia, all over the United States, all over the world. I found myself plugged in to small radio stations in South Dakota, Alaska, talking to little towns of which I had never heard, delivering our brief unhappy statement.

There were other calls, too. From the "crazies." I shall never be inured to the shock of hearing such requests as "Keep the body, do you hear? We can freeze it and bring back this great talent in another generation." Or, "Listen, I know how to do a brain transplant. We can save him—bring him back to life."

I had wanted so much for there to be dignity in the awful process that had to follow the death of such a man. All of us in the hospital wanted that; from my point of view, we succeeded. Despite the carnival atmosphere of TV lights and cameras, despite hundreds of phone calls, legitimate and "crazy," despite the hordes of jostling fans, one message came through clear and strong during that time. We gave John Lennon our all. However, the black-winged bird of death often hovers over our doorstep, not just when a celebrity arrives there. And every single time it does, every nurse, every doctor, and every attendant puts forth his or her strongest efforts to save a life. For those hundreds of other times during the year that the world neither knows about nor cares, for each individual death, we still expend our utmost energies—and weep silently for all those times we cannot make it different.

I believe John Lennon would weep silently for those times, too. As we did for him.